It Takes All Sorts!

(A Look at Life in 1950's Post-War Britain)

Trilogy

Volume I

The Gossips

Karen Barnard

ISBN: 978-1-9999325-0-3
e-Book ISBN: 978-1-9999325-4-1

This paperback edition first published in Great Britain in 2018
by Karen A.K. Barnard

For my Mother and Father

Also by this Author the following books in the Trilogy

It Takes All Sorts!

(A Look at Life in 1950's Post-War Britain)

Volume II The Youngsters

Volume III The Outsiders

Publisher Karen A.K. Barnard

The Gossips

Contents

Introduction

❝ It takes all sorts to make a world", as Badger said to Mole in Kenneth Grahame's timeless, English children's classic '*Wind in the Willows*', (first published in 1908). People are different in character. What might be considered as odd by one person might not be considered odd by another so we should make allowances for people's differences. Individuals may be different and yet they share similar traits in their personalities. They also often share the same values, attitudes and beliefs. All this was no more evident than in the inhabitants of the street I lived in whilst growing up.

Observing people ('people watching', as it is now called), in my neighbourhood, became my hobby as a child growing up. I quickly found out that observing people and events from whatever vantage point, whether it is from a window or in the street, is a fascinating pastime. Especially watching and being a participant in what, in later decades will be history, as it unfolds before one's eyes.

My name is Alison and I would like to introduce you to a world gone by, one that I grew up in, in the first half of the Fifties. The focus of my descriptive narrative is on some of the memorable characters that lived in the street that I also inhabited.

I hope you find these characters as interesting and amusing as I did growing up. They certainly left an indelible impression on my young and inquisitive mind, so much so that I can clearly recall them and the incidents involving them that occurred in our neighbourhood. I remember with fond nostalgia, the idiosyncrasies and habits of the characters I describe that lived in our street.

I had the perfect view from my top, front bedroom window to observe the inhabitants of our neighbourhood and its visitors. From my vantage point, I could see what was going on outside in our street for quite a distance, in both directions. When I wasn't looking out of my bedroom window I was outside on the street.

We youngsters spent most of our young lives out on the street playing or simply idly standing around, or at least most of our spare time, when not attending school or undertaking chores around the home. The deprivations of the post-war years included a lack of toys, so we youngsters had to find our own amusement by using our ingenuity and imaginations. This was often outside and away from under our mothers' watchful eye.

Toy production had all but ceased during the war in order to redeploy what raw materials were available, namely metal, for armament production. Toy manufacturing resumed in earnest after the war; inevitably, though, it took a while for toy production levels to recover to their pre-war output.

The street provided a safe refuge in which to play during the first half of the Fifties since it was mostly free of motor cars and the dangers they entailed, before the proliferation of car ownership in the latter half of the decade. In fact, many residential streets across Britain were designated by the local authorities as, 'Play Streets', although not ours.

The Street Playground Act 1938 gave local authorities the power to prohibit through traffic or restrict traffic in those designated residential streets to specified times during the day. This enabled youngsters to play outside free from the dangers of motor vehicles.

We would happily hang around outside in our street until it was time to go back indoors for bed. So we youngsters were perfectly placed to witness any dramas taking place in our neighbourhood. I was able to observe without arousing suspicion, the comings and goings in my street. The street was our playground and the neighbours and visitors to our street unwittingly provided our entertainment.

The street where I resided, a street situated in a coastal town in the county of Essex in the South-East of England, was typical of any street in any town across Britain. It was a microcosm of society at large in the early to mid-Fifties.

Back then in the early Fifties, there was more social interaction between neighbours, visitors and passers-by. There was the absence of television for the majority to keep people inside their homes. Also, with the absence of motor cars for the masses until the latter half of the decade, people were more visible out on the streets: walking, cycling or using public transport. Cars were almost exclusively reserved for the export market in order to facilitate Britain's economic recovery after the war, and to help to pay off Britain's wartime debts. Basically, the post-war Labour Government's economic policy concentrated on exports to help Britain get back on its feet.

The street and surrounding neighbourhoods were a hive of activity with visiting tradesmen offering their services and wares. This was before the advent of the supermarket where one could buy everything one needed all in one shop, instead of having various tradesmen calling at one's door. This was also before cars were more readily available to transport one's shopping home.

Before supermarkets were a common sight in town centres, people in the first half of the Fifties rubbed shoulders with one another in the time-consuming practice of having to queue at different shops, in order to just purchase one or two items. This parade of shops consisted of the bakery, butcher, grocer, greengrocer, and the fishmonger (particularly if you lived near the coast). There would also be the newsagent-cum-tobacconist and confectioner; the ironmonger (seller of hardware, namely, household implements); cobbler (shoe-repairer), and the haberdasher (seller of sewing articles). People also had to mingle with each other on their journey to and from the shops, either on foot or bicycle or whilst waiting for, and on public transport.

Perishable foods also necessitated daily trips to the shops; this was before the introduction of domestic, labour-saving appliances, such as the refrigerator, which could preserve fresh food for longer. This technological innovation, although readily available to American consumers, only became more affordable for the average consumer here in Britain in the decade that followed. One advantage for me was that it provided me with more opportunities to observe people out in the street going about their daily shopping.

Rationing and general shortages also caused people to have to queue at shops daily for their rations and other goods that were thin on the ground. This allowed me further opportunities to observe all the heightened activity in the neighbourhood.

Food and other commodities and products in Britain were still in short supply in the first half of the Fifties, which is one reason why the government continued enforcing rations; they instituted the rationing system at the start of the Second World War. The wartime coalition government had also introduced rationing in order to prevent people from panic buying and stockpiling food (and other commodities), as they had done during the First World War; prices rose as a result of the shortages. It was also a measure to ensure that food and other essential items were distributed equally among the population; this situation continued after the Second World War. The wartime coalition government had learnt a hard lesson from the experiences of rationing in the First World War.

Britain has always relied heavily on food imports; at least two thirds of its requirements are imported. As an island, Britain relies on boats to import food and other goods. During the First World War German U-boats (submarines) attacked British merchant vessels carrying food imports in an attempt at psychological warfare; the hope was that by starving the population this would force the British Government to capitulate.

With foresight, at the onset of the Second World War the wartime coalition government had to implement rationing well before food ran out; this is why rationing started soon after war broke out in September, 1939. They implemented food rationing, this time, on 8th January, 1940, with further food rationing to follow. (However, they rationed petrol on 22nd September, 1939, a few weeks after the Second World War started.)

In a wartime government initiative, the British population were encouraged to 'Dig for Victory' by growing their own food in their own garden or on public allotments. (Two of the characters that I describe in this first volume of my trilogy, still adhered to this practice. Mr Green grew fruit and vegetables on his small plot in his back garden, as did Reverend Wheatcroft's gardener, in the considerably larger garden adjacent to the vicarage.)

The newly elected Labour Government took the politically expedient measure of continuing the system of rationing in the post-war period. (All rationing finally ceased on 4th July, 1954.) Not only were there dwindling supplies after the war, Britain couldn't afford to pay for imports, as it was heavily in debt. The Labour Government also extended the system of rationing due to its economic policy after the war; this was to reduce imports and increase exports to help with Britain's economic recovery (a point I alluded to earlier). 'Export or Die' was the government's maxim.

Money was needed to pay not only for costly food imports but also for the importation of industrial raw materials. Britain's manufacturing industry was reliant on imported raw materials. Prioritising British products almost exclusively, for the export market, would go some way to redress the balance of payments deficit. Cars were the main export; Britain back then had an iron and steel industry that was vital to the domestic economy, as it had been during the war for manufacturing warships and munitions.

* * *

In order to fully understand the characters and their behaviour in '*It Takes All Sorts!*' my trilogy needs to be understood in the economic, political and social context that pertains to that era, the Fifties. I know reading about dry subjects, such as politics, and in particular economics, is not everyone's cup of tea. However, these topics are relevant to my characters' individual stories so please bear with me. I implore you, please don't let such bare facts and statistics that I present to you in my trilogy '*It Takes All Sorts!*' put you off! The political, economic and social policies that the government of the time, and indeed previous governments' imposed on society, naturally had an impact on the lives of its British citizens; the characters that I have written about were no exception.

The economic, political and social policies and reforms that occurred during the first half of the Fifties provide a backdrop to the human stories that make up my trilogy '*It Takes All Sorts!*' However, the policies and reforms of the previous decade often overlap and have an impact on the following decade, in this instance the Fifties; this phenomenon pertains to any period in history. To this end I have also included those policies pertaining to the immediate post-war years of the previous decade.

The events of the first half of the Fifties with its continued austerity measures of rationing and controls of foodstuffs, goods and services is indeed a legacy of the preceding post-war period of the latter half of the Forties. Even if some of these austerity measures had terminated by the end of the Forties, as in the case of clothes rationing, which came to an end in 1949, (utility clothing ended in 1952), such policies, and indeed reforms, still had an effect on the British psyche. This was certainly true of the characters that I describe in my trilogy.

Included in the major economic, political and social policies and reforms of the Forties was the introduction of sweeping state-run welfare reforms; these reforms had a significant impact on the lives of the British population. These reforms were outlined in the Beveridge Report produced in 1942 (the welfare state had been around since the nineteenth century but was more voluntary-based than state-run). This report laid the foundation for the modern welfare state.

The Beveridge Report, (named after its author, the British economist and social reformer, Sir William Beveridge), set out the principles for eradicating poverty and want from our society. To achieve this goal the government would provide a system of state-funded and comprehensive social security in the form of social insurance provisions and benefits 'from the cradle to the grave'.

The Labour Government implemented a raft of measures to cater for these provisions and benefits. The main measures were the National Insurance Act 1946 and the National Assistance Act 1948. Whilst a comprehensive National Health Service (NHS), included as part of the overall plan in the Beveridge Report, provided free health care for all at the point of delivery, regardless of income. The National Health Service Act 1946 came into force on 5th July, 1948.

The 1944 Education Act, led to further reforms in the education system. The Conservative-led wartime coalition government introduced this Act. It is often referred to as the 'Butler Act' since the Conservative politician and President of the Board of Education, Richard Austen 'Rab' Butler, steered this bill through Parliament. It provided universal free secondary education. The Act also raised the school-leaving age from fourteen to fifteen, (which came into effect in 1947). Secondary education would be provided under the tripartite system, consisting of the grammar school, technical school and the secondary modern.

The post-war Labour Government supported the tripartite system; in doing so it could be argued that they failed to adhere to the socialist principle of providing equal educational opportunity to all, which an all-inclusive, comprehensive school would have provided. Post-war Labour Ministers of Education, Ellen Wilkinson and her successor George Tomlinson both supported selection and hence the grammar schools, they were therefore both keen to implement the tripartite system. (I consider the ramifications of this educational system on its pupils in my descriptive narrative of Reverend Wheatcroft, which follows this introduction, and also in the introduction, and character portrayal of Jeremy, a grammar school pupil, in Volume II of my trilogy.)

The Labour Party won the first general election after the war by a major landslide on 25th July, 1945, mainly on the socialist policies I have described. Their promises of social reform with their enticing electoral slogan, 'Let Us Face the Future', struck a cord with the British electorate. Their shock, sweeping victory ousted Sir Winston Churchill.

The Labour Party's win removed from power the former coalition wartime, unelected Prime Minister and leader of the Conservative Party, Sir Winston Churchill who had led us victoriously through the war years. The British population were fed up with the hardships they had to endure during the war and so were hungry for social change; this partly explains the Labour Party's electoral victory in 1945.

Winning an overall majority of seats for the first time in the history of the Labour Party enabled them to push through these major reforms, such as the inception of the National Health Service. This was arguably their greatest achievement to date. These achievements made by the Labour Government are all a legacy from the Forties, which naturally impacted on the Fifties. In turn, these social welfare policies impacted on the lives of the British people, and indeed, on the lives of the characters that inhabited the street I grew up in. These welfare policies also, of course, impacted on the lives of the population in the decades that followed.

* * *

The population here in Britain in the first half of the Fifties were however, generally worse off compared to other countries that had been affected by the war. This was even the case when compared to the aggressors of the war, Germany. West Germany was experiencing rapid economic growth in the Fifties. (However, this was in stark contrast to communist controlled East Germany who fared far worse than their counterparts in West Germany.) The British population had to endure rationing and shortages for a longer period than most of the other countries involved in the war. The Second World War had left Britain virtually bankrupt. Financing the war had crippled Britain's economy. The British Government had borrowed heavily from the United States of America, (as they had done in the First World War) to help finance the war and Britain was now heavily in debt.

Under the Lend-Lease programme, during the Second World War, the United States Government provided military aid and other assistance to Britain and its other allies. The United States lent Britain essential supplies of military hardware, clothing and foodstuffs, with the proviso that they would receive reciprocal aid from Britain. Britain's reverse lend-lease contributions consisted mainly in supplying aid to American soldiers serving abroad. Under President Roosevelt's leadership, the United States Government set up this Agreement on 11th March, 1941; however, they terminated it without warning, on 2nd September, 1945.

The British Government's chief Economist John Maynard Keynes, managed to negotiate a subsequent 'Anglo-American Loan Agreement', (a form of credit), in the post-war era, on 15th July, 1946; this time Britain had to pay for the loan. (The US loan was only paid off on 29th December, 2006!)

This subsequent loan was vital for Britain in the post-war era. The newly elected Labour Government had embarked on a huge and costly social reform programme, constructing the welfare state. Britain also needed the loan to pay for costly food imports (one of the reasons why rationing was continued, as I alluded to earlier). Britain also had a crippling balance of payments deficit, as I also pointed out earlier.

Britain received further aid from the United States under the Foreign Assistance Act of 1948. This European Recovery Programme (ERP), popularly known as the Marshall Plan, (named after the Secretary of State George C. Marshall who was the originator of the plan) provided economic aid (Marshall Aid) after the Second World War. It was to help facilitate the recovery and post-war reconstruction of war-torn Europe.

The loan would help Britain to rebuild its infrastructure and industries after the devastating and costly Second World War. Britain's United States benefactor was, of course, also motivated by political concerns that would be detrimental to their economy. Their plan to build-up the fragile economies of European countries devastated by the war, was also motivated by their desire to ensure that they had prosperous European markets; Europe has always provided an important market for United States exports of goods and services. The United States Government also wanted to bolster capitalism and unify Europe against the threat of communism that was threatening to encroach from Eastern Europe.

Communism was already a threatening force in Greece in 1947 and in Turkey. Since Britain was no longer able to afford financial aid to Greece and Turkey, the United States Government supplied immediate military and economic assistance to these European countries. This emergency aid resulted in the Truman Doctrine, introduced by President Truman in March 1947. This foreign policy pledged that the United States would provide aid to countries like Greece and Turkey so that they would be better equipped to resist take-over by a totalitarian regime, namely communist rule. Marshall Aid followed soon after in June of that year, to help other struggling countries in Europe (and elsewhere) to resist communism.

Britain was in receipt of more aid than other countries in Europe who had accepted Marshall Aid, (even West Germany was a recipient). However, Britain used the financial aid primarily on funding and maintaining Britain's role as a world power; this was done at the expense of using the funds for reconstructing Britain's infrastructure and industries at home. Marshall Aid funding ended in 1951.

The Labour Government's decision to continue to invest in the maintenance of Britain's military commitments overseas exacerbated the economic crisis. Even the NHS became a casualty of defence expenditure in 1952. The outbreak of the Communist War in Korea in 1950, which involved British troops, caused the Chancellor of the Exchequer Hugh Gaitskell, to impose prescription charges (on spectacles and dentures) for the first time, in 1951. (These charges were implemented by the Conservative Government the following year.) This NHS charge and the unrealistic expenditure on rearmament caused several prominent Government Ministers to resign. (I discuss this incident in more detail in my character portrayal of the young, newly married couple featured in this volume and in my character portrayal of Jeremy in Volume II of my trilogy.)

The Labour Government extended national service for all fit and able young men after the Second World War to help oversee Britain's increasing defence commitments overseas during the post-war era. They were sent to strengthen the peacekeeping force composed of the regular men and women already serving in the armed forces in those areas. They served in Europe, the Middle East, Asia, and in Africa. A reserve of troops would also be required in readiness for war, should another war involving Britain ever break out again.

British reservists served overseas in Palestine in the Middle East during the political unrest, which ended in 1948, when the British terminated its mandate. The British Government declared a state of emergency in Malaya, in South-East Asia, in June, 1948, and sent troops there. (The country was re-named Malaysia in 1963.)

While in North-East Asia, a Communist War broke out between North and South Korea, in June, 1950; British reservists were despatched there to fight as part of the United Nations forces. (I elaborate on what is often referred to as Britain's 'forgotten war' in Korea, in several of the narratives in my trilogy '*It Takes All Sorts!*')

Britain also declared a state of emergency in Kenya, in East Africa, in October, 1952, and sent British reservists to deal with the Mau Mau uprising (also referred to as the Mau Mau rebellion). National service conscripts also served in other spots in the Middle East, and elsewhere in the world.

The characters that feature in this volume of my trilogy were all familiar with the ramifications of national service. They had either experienced the impact themselves, as in the case of the young, newly married couple, or they knew of others in their neighbourhood who had, or were still serving as conscripts. Indeed, Reverend Wheatcroft felt it his Christian duty to help families with serving relatives, through these difficult times.

* * *

Maintaining Britain's security and its place as a world leader was of paramount importance after the Second World War. Britain was a member of the recently formed United Nations (UN) and its UN Security Council, one of the principal organs of the United Nations. The UN was created on 24th October, 1945; its aim was to secure international peace and security.

Britain also became a member of the North Atlantic Treaty Organisation (NATO), which was created on 4[t.h] April, 1949. The Truman Doctrine led to the formation of NATO. It was a military alliance between the United States, Canada, Britain and several other West European countries all bordering the North Atlantic Ocean. NATO would provide collective security against the Soviet

16

Union and its threat of communist expansion in Western Europe. The Soviet Union's response was to form, with several Eastern European countries, their own political and military alliance. The Warsaw Treaty Organisation was established on 14th May, 1955, commonly referred to as the 'Warsaw Pact'.

The West viewed the Soviet Union as the new threat to world peace; the Soviet Union now occupied much of Eastern Europe after World War Two. (These communist regimes would later be known as the Eastern Bloc.) Churchill had delivered his famous Cold War 'iron curtain' speech at a college in the United States on 5th March, 1946, in which he expressed his fears that "… an iron curtain has descended across the Continent. Behind that line lie all the capitals …of Central and Eastern Europe…in what I must call the Soviet sphere…"

Cold War tensions began to show after World War Two had ended. These tensions were revealed in peace talks that took place at the close of the war and just after the war: the Yalta Conference in February, 1945, and the subsequent Potsdam Conference in July and August 1945.

The Yalta peace meeting took place between all three world leaders: British coalition Prime Minister, Winston Churchill, the United States President, Franklin D. Roosevelt and Soviet Premier, Joseph Stalin. They met to discuss and plan war-torn Europe's political reconstruction, which included Germany, after the war. The Soviet Union was, in effect, given control over Eastern Europe.

At the Potsdam Conference further peace talks took place with the three world leaders: (Prime Minster Clement Atlee had replaced Winston Churchill due to a General Election, and President Harry S. Truman had replaced President Roosevelt who had died). The results of that meeting left President Truman, in particular, fearful of further communist expansion, hence his introduction of the Truman Doctrine in 1947 to counter this threat.

The spread of communism was further realised in the 1948 Berlin Blockade crisis, also referred to as the 'Berlin Airlift'. After the war, Germany was divided into four zones of occupation, including the capital Berlin, (decided at the Potsdam Conference). West Berlin was controlled by the United States, Britain and France, while the Soviet Union controlled East Berlin. In March, 1948, the three Western Allies unified their individual zones and proposed and later introduced (in June), a new currency for West Germany; this met with opposition from the Soviets. The Soviet Union responded in June, 1948, by blockading West Berlin by road, rail and canal through Soviet occupied zones in East Berlin (Berlin is situated in East Germany); in doing so they prevented vital supplies from getting through to the population in West Germany. They believed the three Western Allies would acquiesce.

The Western Allies found a solution to the blockade, they would airlift food, fuel, medicine and other supplies into West Berlin, (the Allies had previously secured right of way over a few air corridors over East Berlin into West Berlin). The Western Allies made over two hundred thousand air sorties during the blockade, delivering over two hundred million tons of supplies, an unprecedented feat! The Soviet Union finally lifted the blockade almost a year later, in 1949. The Berlin Blockade incident highlighted the friction between East and West Germany that eventually led to the building of the Berlin Wall in 1961, which separated East Germany from West. Germany.

The fear of communist expansion gained momentum in the United States, in the first half of the Fifties. The red scare had been prevalent in the Thirties and particularly in the late Forties. The Federal Bureau of Investigation (FBI) was heavily involved in rooting out threats to national security, under the leadership of its director J. Edgar Hoover. The FBI targeted all levels of American society for their criminal investigations. Acting on tip offs, they investigated employees working for the public and private sector; all were subjected to the FBI's rigorous investigations. Even private citizens didn't escape from scrutiny by the FBI.

The 'House of Un-American Activities Committee' (HUAC), was a congressional committee set up in 1938, to investigate and try those persons suspected of alleged disloyalty and subversion, namely communism. A well publicised case brought before the House, in 1947, involved employees working specifically in the entertainment industry. This particular industry had been targeted during the Forties for harbouring communists or fellow travellers (communist sympathisers). Under aggressive investigation at the Committee Hearing, witnesses were forced to name names. They would be asked the infamous question: "Are you now, or have you ever been a member of the Communist Party?" Many were blacklisted as a result of being brought before the House, which caused them to lose their jobs and prevented them from gaining work in the entertainment Industry.

Republican Senator Joseph McCarthy provoked a new wave of communist hysteria in the United States after he gave his infamous speech on communist infiltration. He delivered his speech to the stunned audience of a Women's Republican Club in Wheeling, West Virginia on February 9th, 1950. In his dramatic speech he employed alarming rhetoric; he claimed that there was "treason in high government", that there were "enemies from within" the State Department, which was "infested with communists". What is more, those names were known to be "card-carrying members or certainly loyal to the Communist Party, but who nevertheless are still helping to shape our foreign policy".

The era of McCarthyism culminated in 1953, in tomecide, that is, book burning subversive books. McCarthy's team of investigators trawled public libraries and educational libraries, including United States Information Service Libraries overseas for subversive material. The offensive material was either burned or removed from shelves.

The era of McCarthyism effectively came to an end when Senator McCarthy, who based his accusations of communism on unsubstantiated evidence, was subjected to censure by the Senate in December, 1954. He had turned his attentions on the United States Army in 1954, known as the Army-McCarthy Hearings; (these Hearings were televised), in which he charged the United States Army with being "soft" on communism. Bringing the United States Army into disrepute was considered by many, including the former Army General and now President Dwight D. (Ike) Eisenhower, as a step too far.

(Rooting out security risks, that is, communist subversion still continued unabated in many organisations and formal groups; they still subjected their employees, job applicants and members to loyalty oaths. One notable example is the State of California, since 1950, the Constitution of the State of California has required all its state employees to sign the loyalty oath.)

The anti-communist paranoia in the United States had also highlighted cases of communist espionage both in America (Hiss, the Rosenbergs', and Oppenheimer) and over here in Britain. (Fuchs,

Burgess and MacLean). (I elaborate on these individual cases in my character portrayal of our 'Mystery Man' in Volume III of my trilogy.)

* * *

On the home front in Britain, housing was a priority after the war, (as it had been before the war), to clear the slums and rebuild. Indeed, housing was now critical. The post-war baby boom, (which peaked in Britain in 1946), reinforced the urgent demand for housing; accommodating the growing families of returning servicemen was now a pressing problem, as it had been after the First World War. (It was certainly a pressing problem for our young, newly married couple who had to endure residing with their nosey landlady Mrs Trenchard, until they could afford to move out.)

There was an increased lack of adequate housing due not only to general neglect of old housing stock, and lack of materials and manpower (used for the war effort) but also due to the devastating bomb damage inflicted during the Blitz. The Luftwaffe's aerial, pilotless V1's and V2's, an abbreviation for Vergeltungswaffen (retaliatory weapons), commonly referred to as 'vengeance weapons', were responsible for much of the damage. The V-1 missiles, (the world's first cruise missiles) and the V-2 rockets (the world's first long-range, guided ballistic missiles) left in their wake scarred towns and cities across Britain.

The winged V-1 missiles were nicknamed 'buzz bombs' because of the terrifying mechanical drone these pilotless aircraft made; this pulsating, rasping noise would cut out when the engine stopped and landed on its target. Another nickname was 'doodlebugs' (a flying, larvae insect with wings (ant lion) that makes a buzzing sound). The more lethal V-2 rockets were programmed to fly on a guided, predetermined course and distance but often missed their target, a major city, mainly London, by many miles! However, British Intelligence did send bogus reports that the rockets were overshooting their intended target. The Luftwaffe's sustained aerial bombing campaign caused heavy casualties, with even more civilians left homeless.

The newly elected Labour Government led by Prime Minister Clement Atlee had an electoral mandate to improve people's living conditions; they would achieve this by providing adequate housing.

Housing was on their list of reforms, along with other reforms, some of which I have already mentioned. (These reforms included the nationalisation of industries, the formation of the National Health Service, and the National Insurance Scheme.)

The Labour Government's housing programme included the building of 300,000 new homes a year, (mainly new council houses after the slum clearance). However, they had to put their ambitious housing programme on the backburner as they concentrated their efforts on paying back the American loans. The production of goods for export, such as motor cars, would go some way to achieving this aim, a point I made earlier. Britain dominated the world market for manufacturing cars in the Fifties, and was certainly the biggest exporter of cars in the early Fifties. The government therefore prioritised production for export.

Britain's financial crisis resulted in the British people having to endure going without for longer than any of their counterparts, a point I touched on earlier; this period of restraint lasted for a prolonged period totalling fourteen years. These years were referred to as the era of, 'Austerity', a course of economic constraints imposed by the then Minister for Economic Affairs (a newly created office in 1947) and Chancellor of the Exchequer, Sir (Richard) Stafford Cripps.

It was in part due to these austerity measures, which led to the Labour Government scraping through with a substantially reduced majority, at the next General Election, on 23rd February, 1950. The Labour Government's misfortunes took a further downturn with the extra financial burden of a heavy rearmament defence budget due to the Korean War, a war which began on 25th June, 1950.

These factors, in turn, caused another hastily called General Election on 25th October, 1951, in which Labour lost to the Conservatives, led once more by the charismatic leader Sir Winston Churchill. (Although it must be pointed out that the Labour Party achieved far more votes overall than the Conservative Party but won less parliamentary seats; this is due to the vagaries of the first-past-the-post voting system, which, of course, is still in place today.) It is also worthy of note that the Labour Party won more votes in the 1951 General Election than at any time in their history to date.

Ironically, the electoral promises the Labour Party had made for social reform led, in part, to their downfall. Although to their credit, the Labour Party had achieved many of their reforms, such as the nationalisation of key industries. The railways were nationalised in 1947. The coal industry was nationalised in 1946, and came into effect on 1st January, 1947. The gas and electricity industries were nationalised in 1948. Nationalisation of the iron and steel industry, under the Iron and Steel Act 1949, took effect in 1951. (However, the iron and steel industry had a chequered history. These industries were first nationalised in 1951, denationalised in 1953, renationalised in 1967, and finally, denationalised in 1988!)

In spite of the Labour Government's reforms, however, people were still having to endure austerity with controls on private consumption, and continued shortages and rationing of goods. The Conservatives, with their electoral promise and enticing slogan to 'Set the People Free' now appealed to the voter. Ironically, although Labour had managed to rebuild a million or so homes, they had not fulfilled their rash election promise to build 300,000 homes a year; this was a pledge, which the Conservative Government took up in earnest.

In the interim, due to the lack of housing, people had to endure living in cramped conditions. This often meant remaining in the family home or being forced to share accommodation in rented premises. However, living in rented accommodation was not a recent phenomenon, as this type of housing was common in the Victorian era, right up to the Fifties. Neighbours back in the first half of the Fifties were still often living cheek by jowl.

Living in such close proximity has a tendency to breed gossip, much to my delight growing up in that era. Neighbours with nothing better to do in-between their daily household chores would amuse themselves by gossiping about what was going on in their street and neighbourhood. (The characters I describe in this first volume: Mrs Green, Mrs Trenchard, and the vicar's housekeeper Miss Herbert, provided most of the gossip in our street.)

Naturally, residents were more concerned about what was happening on their own doorstep, that is, in their street and in their neighbourhood. They had few links to the outside world, which was of course, provided by the radio, the newspaper and the British Pathe Newsreels of world events shown at the local cinemas. Also, relatives, friends or acquaintances, having just returned from fighting in the armed forces overseas in the war, provided another link to the outside world. Also young men in the armed forces, who had undertaken or were undertaking their national service abroad, provided another connection with the world outside. As, of course, did the influx of foreign war refugees and immigrants from Europe.

The British Government actively encouraged immigrants to work in Britain after the war to help with the reconstruction of Britain. There was a severe labour shortage. Irish workers, in particular, helped to fill the gaps in the labour market. Also included in this group of immigrants, were those from the commonwealth: from the Caribbean and from the Indian subcontinent. The British Nationality Act 1948, allowed all citizens of the commonwealth free entry into Britain. (Ireland ceased being part of the commonwealth in 1949, when they became the Republic of Ireland; however, they were still allowed entry into Britain to work.) The first Caribbean immigrants to arrive in Britain arrived on the British ship the Empire Windrush, which docked at Tilbury Docks on the River Thames, in Essex. All these new immigrants provided a labour force that was much needed in Britain to aid its economic recovery in the post-war period.

Neighbours' congregating out on the street was commonplace back then, so I was able to observe and overhear a lot of the goings-on in our street. (This was especially the case, in the presence of our street's resident gossips.) The street provided a breeding ground for gossip, where secrets didn't last long and where neighbours' business was a free for all. It was like living as one large family or as part of a kinship, played out in the street and neighbourhood.

Of course, once new housing became available in the newly created towns and estates built in the post-war period, people became more socially mobile. (The young, newly married couple featured in this first volume, eventually moved out to the suburbs, so I heard on the grapevine.) These new homes sprung up in the suburbs, on land beyond the green belt and away from the urban sprawl with its slums and bomb damaged sites. These new areas of living, on open, green spaces are often referred to as 'garden cities'. Urban dwellers moved away from the neighbourhood and the neighbours they knew so well. This new phenomenon brought to an end what was once known as the 'community spirit'; people became increasingly isolated from one another in these new, unfamiliar and faraway towns.

Social interaction was also a feature of people's leisure pursuits in the first half of the Fifties. Attending the cinema, or going to the 'pictures' as it was universally called, was the most popular pastime back in the early Fifties. The Fifties was still the golden age of the cinema. The big movie star names of the silver screen had the pulling power to attract audiences who flocked to the cinema to watch their favourite stars. (It was certainly Mr Green's favourite leisure pursuit; once inside the cinema he could escape from the general hardships endured in those lean, post-war years and from living with his embittered spouse.)

The favourite film genres watched by filmgoers in the Fifties were historical adventures and dramas, biblical epics, westerns, and romantic musicals; these were, in the main, produced by the American film capital of the world: Hollywood. Then of course, there were the popular American and British-made films about the Second World War, (which were favourites of Mr Green). These war films were a great morale booster; World War Two, of course, was still fresh in peoples' memories. Also popular with British filmgoers, were the British-made Ealing comedies produced in the post-war period. The British needed something to laugh about; humour offered a release from the horrors and hardships suffered during the recently ended war and from living in the bleak Age of Austerity that followed. These Ealing comedies produced by the London-based Ealing Studios are now considered classics. This was all before watching the television became a mainstream activity in the home.

Before television the radio (wireless), the gramophone (record player) and the radiogram (radio and gramophone combined) provided the mainstay for home entertainment, apart from the piano. Virtually every home had an upright piano, which was housed in the front room. Family members would gather round the piano for sing-songs at Christmas time and on other special occasions.

The first live, televised, international outside broadcast of the Coronation of Queen Elizabeth the Second, on 2nd June, 1953, had a marked impact on people's viewing and listening habits; it helped to popularise to the masses the joys of watching this relatively new medium. It was the first international, outside broadcast of a live,

24

major event. Television viewing was a minority activity prior to the Queen's Coronation in 1953.

The first major outside broadcast had been the televised Coronation procession route of the Queen's late father King George the Sixth and her mother Queen Elizabeth, on 12th May, 1937; television as a medium was still in its infancy at the time, with only a limited number of viewers. The Coronation in 1953 was also of historical significance because it was the first time that cameras were allowed inside Westminster Abbey to film the actual event, as it happened. The previous Coronation of King George the Sixth, in 1937, did not allow cameras inside Westminster Abbey.

The exciting prospect of watching the Coronation of Queen Elizabeth the Second live on television, prompted many people to purchase a set, or at least acquire one on hire-purchase; (this was particularly so when borrowing restrictions were finally lifted in the second half of the decade). Or after having watched this spectacular event on someone else's television or seen a screening at a large public gathering in a community centre, persuaded viewers to acquire their own set. The Home Office granted collective TV licences to public places, such as, the local town hall, dance hall, cinema, pub, hospital, and even the church, in order to allow people to watch the televised Coronation event at these venues.

(Mr and Mrs Green were one of the lucky ones to purchase a television in time for the Coronation. Mr Green had always been keen to acquire a television set. Mrs Green finally relented, when it dawned on her that acquiring a television set would allow her to broaden her horizons by being nosey about other people's lives beyond the confines of her street and neighbourhood.)

Thereafter, more people (like Mr and Mrs Green) preferred to stay inside their own homes watching the 'little box in the corner'. So rather than being active participants in the human drama played out on the street, people became increasingly isolated from what was going on outside their homes. Instead, they became passive viewers to what was being shown 'on the box'. Television viewing peaked in the Fifties, both here in Britain and in the United States; this is why many view the Fifties as the golden age of television. Unfortunately for me, this was to have an adverse effect on my pastime of observing the comings and goings in my street.

Active participation, as oppose to passive participation in leisure pursuits however, was also popular during the first half of the Fifties. Dancing was the most popular participant leisure activity in Britain. Fishing (angling: fishing with a rod and line) was the most popular participant sport. (Angling was a favourite pursuit of Mr Green, whilst dancing was a favourite pastime of our young, newly married couple.)

Of course, people also congregated outside their homes to participate in spectator sport, such as football (soccer), the most popular spectator sport back then, as it is today. One much talked about football match back then was the 1953, FA (Football Association) Cup Final, when Blackpool beat Bolton Wanderers to win the Cup. This historic match took place at the Wembley stadium in London, the month before the Coronation, on 2nd May, 1953. (Naturally, Mr Green was also a fan of football, any excuse to spend time away from his nagging spouse!)

Cricket was also a popular spectator sport in Britain in the Fifties. The historic match when England regained the Ashes on home ground at the Oval, after nineteen years, on 19th August, 1953, lives on in peoples' memories. (Reverend Wheatcroft and Mr Green were both cricket fans.) Greyhound racing was another popular spectator sport, second only to football.

Horse racing was yet another popular spectator sport. A historic race took place in the same week as the Coronation, on 6th June, 1953, when jockey Sir Gordon Richards famously won the Epsom Derby on his horse Pinza, at his twenty-eighth attempt!

People also attended national public events, such as the, Festival of Britain, which was held to celebrate Britain's recovery from the war. This Festival opened in the spring, on 3rd May, 1951, and closed in the autumn, on 30th September of that year. The Festival attracted record crowds, an estimated eight and a half million people attended. (Our young, newly married couple were among the attendees.) The Festival was also to coincide with the centenary of the Great Exhibition of 1851. In effect, it was a huge trade fair, showcasing Britain's achievements in science, technology, the arts and industrial design.

The Festival turned out to be a resounding commercial success; however, there was much criticism at the time, due to the exorbitant cost of staging it. The Festival cost the Labour Government eleven million pounds out of a budget of twelve million pounds. Many people thought it was a waste of public money when the country was still subjected to rationing and shortages.

The British people were also invited to celebrate the Coronation of Queen Elizabeth the Second, on 2nd June, 1953. They did so in an enthusiastic display of patriotism. It was as if they were participating in one big happy, united family affair. People lined the procession route to observe the historical proceedings unfold with the Gold State Coach making its way to Westminster Abbey, containing the soon to be crowned new Queen. Or they observed the Coronation ceremony, as it happened, live on television. Street residents in towns and villages throughout Britain also held street parties, with their street decked out in Union Jack flags; they also participated in other public events during that spring and summer. This event gave me another opportunity to observe people at close quarters.

* * *

My trilogy, '*It Takes All Sorts!*' describes how people lived their lives back in the first half of the Fifties, in an age characterised by strict adherence to conformity and rules. Britain back in the Fifties was a conservative, authoritarian and class-ridden society. It was also an inherently religious society in the Fifties; Britain did not become a. more secular society until the latter half of the next decade. The majority of people still attended church and believed in God. (This is why I have included our local vicar, Reverend Wheatcroft in my trilogy. Reverend Wheatcroft played such an intrinsic role in our neighbourhood. I start this first volume in my trilogy with a character portrayal of him. The character portrayal that follows features Mr and Mrs Green who were not only regular churchgoers but also helped out in the church in a voluntary capacity.)

'*It Takes All Sorts!*' examines peoples' attitudes, values and beliefs. It portrays their domestic, social and working lives. It also reveals how people travelled, how they dressed; the homes they lived in and how these were furnished. It describes the food they ate and what they drank. It also examines leisure pursuits: what people read, listened to and watched, and generally, what they did for recreation. Included, are the new inventions and achievements in science and technology that took place in the early to mid-Fifties. It also includes the cultural arts (covering literature, music, film, fashion and sport) that defined the first half of the Fifties.

Major events, such as the Festival of Britain, held in 1951, successfully showed to the world that Britain and its people were resilient in the face of adversity. It promoted Britain's past achievements and heralded Britain's new innovations for the future, in the fields of technology and industry, science, manufacturing, and the arts, and in particular, lifestyle changes.

The Festival showcased revolutionary, labour-saving appliances and new contemporary designs for the domestic market. These products were not affordable at the time for the average British consumer who was still subjected to rations and shortages; instead those products on display at the Festival offered a taste of things to come and to aspire to have in the future. The modernist architecture and urban design on show at the Festival was a feature of post-war housebuilding and featured in the design and construction of the newly created towns.

(The innovations on display at the Festival were of interest to our young, newly married couple; they were dreaming of the day when they could finally set up home together and create their own home in the new contemporary style with all the latest labour-saving appliances that they had seen at the show. Labour-saving appliances were also of interest to Mrs Green so that she could devote more time to her favourite hobby of standing around in the street gossiping!)

The Coronation of Queen Elizabeth the Second, on 2nd June, 1953, heralded the dawn of a new era, the 'New Elizabethan Age'. It inspired new achievements in the field of human endeavour. Relayed to the world on the eve of the Coronation was news of the conquest of the summit of the tallest mountain in the world, Mount Everest. Mountaineers Edmund Hillary and Tenzing Norgay achieved this feat of human endurance; they finally conquered what had before been an unattainable goal.

Such momentous events inspired the population with hope and optimism for a new beginning, a future where anything seemed possible. On 6th May, 1954, Roger Bannister made possible the four-minute mile run when he achieved this previously insurmountable feat of human endurance. He also inspired others to achieve what had before seemed an impossible feat and better it. While the end of all rationing at midnight on 4th July, 1954, signalled the end of austerity and controls and the start of a rapidly changing, more affluent, consumer society.

* * *

The characters I have portrayed in my trilogy '*It Takes All Sorts!*' are typical of characters that could just as easily have inhabited any street in Britain at that time in Britain's history. Indeed, many of their personality traits are not just typical of the particular era of the Fifties; they are pertinent to society today.

I have selected both young and old, conformist and eccentric, and from different social classes. All were living in the same environment, an era marked by years of austerity and controls and a time when dramatic changes were occurring in this post-war age.

These character portraits do not have to be read in any particular order; indeed these individual portraits stand alone as separate descriptive narratives. Each chapter contains a miniature portrait of a particular character or characters that lived in (or visited in the case of our local vicar) the street where I grew up. To this end, I have repeated both national and world events, economic, political and social policies and reforms, and general facts, as they pertain to each character.

I have divided these individual portraits into three parts and present these in the form of a trilogy. This format allows for a narrative break. The individual character portrayals are grouped together to provide three distinct parts; these parts are all connected by a central theme, time and place. A typical, residential street in Britain during the Fifties provides the setting for each volume. Described within each volume, are a group of characters who all resided in (or visited) this particular street during the first half of the Fifties.

Volume I provides character portraits of '*The Gossips*' who resided in our street. Gossips are, of course, endemic in a close-knit community.

Volume II portrays '*The Youngsters*' who lived in our street. This is the era of the post-war baby boomers, so the neighbourhood was bound to have their fair share of youngsters.

Volume III provides character portraits of individuals who lived in our street, all of whom were treated as '*The Outsiders*' by the other neighbours. They didn't quite fit in; society back in the first half of the Fifties was, as I stated earlier, staunchly conformist, conservative and authoritarian. Their differences tended to isolate them from the rest of the neighbourhood; they met with prejudice because of their differences. Suspicions were also heightened during this era of the Cold War; anyone who was different, an outsider, became a target of suspicion.

* * *

In this first volume of my trilogy I have included character portraits of 'Our Local Vicar, Reverend Wheatcroft Who Lived on The Other Side of Town'; 'A Retired Couple, Mr and Mrs Green Who Lived Opposite', and 'A Young, Newly Married Couple Who Lodged Nearby With Their Landlady Mrs Trenchard'.

I begin with a character portrait of Reverend Wheatcroft who was our local vicar. Although, technically he didn't live in our street, he often visited it to call on his parishioners, and played such an intrinsic role in the life of our community. In particular, he played such an important part in my education and that of my young contemporaries' growing up in that era. I certainly learnt a lot from him. His presence in our neighbourhood had a profound effect on my intellectual and moral development. He became a great role model for me, as a child growing up.

He was one of my favourites. I admired him for his intelligence, wit, humour and kindness. He was certainly perceptive enough to interpret the behaviour and motivations of his parishioners. He was also not immune from human foibles himself, and would not profess to be perfect and above human frailties, which only made him all the more likable in my eyes. He could be artful to get his own way, but he tempered this with a good nature and sense of humour. His weakness for food and drink, especially his sweet tooth, which may have just surpassed even my own and my contemporaries' love of all things sweet, was often amusingly in evidence.

Reverend Wheatcroft was, of course, familiar with local gossip. His job as the local parish vicar required him to take an objective interest in the lives of his parishioners; this meant that he would invariably come across idle gossip and rumour. But he had to be discreet with what he heard, or was told in his capacity as the local vicar. He would have to turn a blind eye and listen with only half an ear to all the tittle-tattle that he invariably came across in his post. Rather than indulging in gossip he often became the subject of gossip.

His housekeeper was guilty of being a gossipmonger. She gossiped about Reverend Wheatcroft, but with her there was no malicious intent. She was simply proud to be in the service of her employer whom she held in such high regard. She was therefore keen to let the members of his congregation know she was indispensable to him. Reverend Wheatcroft relied upon the services of his loyal housekeeper to run the household and manage his domestic affairs. What is more, she let it be known that by taking over these roles she enabled him to spend the majority of his time carrying out his religious duties, which was to serve his parishioners in the neighbourhood. Thus she felt she had an important role to play. It gave her a purpose in life; I don't think she had any other living family.

Our street was no different to any other street in that it also had its resident gossips. Mrs Green was one of the street's renowned gossips. I found the lengths she went to, to be nosey and listen in on other people's conversations, highly amusing. There was plenty happening in our street back then, (as I suspect, there would be in any other street), which provided juicy fodder for her gossip. She had an insatiable appetite for gossip and would keep an ever watchful eye (as I did) on all the comings and goings in our street.

Mrs Green probably had enough ammunition to write a book herself, if she was at all like me, literarily inclined. Somehow, I didn't think so; she indulged in this hobby of hers, purely for her own amusement, when she had nothing else as interesting to preoccupy her time. (Generally, married women did not work in the Fifties era of the stay-at-home housewife, as they had done during the war when they took over men's work roles while the men were off fighting in the war.)

She was married to Mr Green. Unlike his spouse, Mr Green was very unassuming and preferred to keep himself to himself. Mr Green was retired; the couple therefore had plenty of time on their hands to get in each other's way. Mr Green made strenuous attempts to avoid this by indulging in various outdoor pursuits, when he was able to.

They made an odd couple in my humble opinion; they appeared to be totally unsuited to one another, as different as chalk and cheese. Nevertheless, I suspect, they, like many long married and long suffering couples, put on a brave front for the neighbours, as divorce was a relatively new phenomenon, and on the whole, frowned upon in those days.

A young, newly married couple, Daphne and Dennis, lived nearby. They unfortunately had to start off married life under the same roof as their nosey and gossiping landlady Mrs Trenchard, and her cunning cat, Humphrey. (Most couples followed convention by marrying before living together in those days. They also married young; in their early twenties was the norm.)

Like many young, married couples at the time, they couldn't yet afford to set up home together so they had to endure living with their landlady. It was the norm back then for a married couple to live with their parents, usually the bride's parents, until they could afford to move into a place of their own. Besides, there was of course, a general lack of housing available due to bomb damage during the war and due to dilapidated properties (slums), which were often uninhabitable.

The Labour Government had to put their plans for slum clearance and their housebuilding programme on the backburner due to other pressing financial commitments, a point that I made earlier in this introduction. This meant that the young couple had to patiently wait their turn for the ambitious house rebuilding programme to come to fruition, which both the Labour and Conservative Governments in turn, had pledged to build. I overheard all the trials and tribulations of this young couple who had the misfortune of having to live under the watchful eye of their gossiping landlady; it was a revelation to me.

Mrs Trenchard was responsible for most of the gossip regarding her young tenants. The reader gets an insight into the extent of her gossip and the effect it had on this young couple through their revelations. They reveal Mrs Trenchard's shortcomings, namely her gossiping nature, in their account of the goings-on at the house they resided in with her at the helm.

Finally, I wish to reiterate that my trilogy '*It Takes All Sorts!*' is a work of fiction. Any resemblance to actual persons and incidents relating to them, living or dead is purely coincidental, except in the case of historical fact. I also wish to add that I have tried to be accurate with regard to dates of actual facts and factual events, where my memory serves me, backed up by meticulous research; any errors are therefore entirely my own.

Our Local Vicar, Reverend Wheatcroft Who Lived On the Other Side of Town

I saw a lot of our local vicar, Reverend Wheatcroft, although, technically he didn't live in our street, he was a regular visitor to our street. He lived in the local vicarage. Of course, we had other regular visitors to our street, such as the tradesmen: the milkman, bread man, grocer, greengrocer, postman, coalman, rag-and-bone man, and even a fishmonger (because we lived in a coastal town), and the general salesmen selling bits and bobs, and the ice-cream seller in the summer. Our vicar's trade was spiritual guidance. He provided us with something more than mere sustenance for our stomachs, he provided us with spiritual sustenance.

I would usually see him in our street on his trusted bicycle; I understood that he had been a keen cyclist in his youth. However, most people back then did cycle on short journeys, or walked or caught the bus. Later, towards the middle fifties, I would spot him driving around in a mid-grey coloured Morris Minor Traveller two-door estate car with its distinctive feature, namely, a wooden frame surround to the rear body. He would be visiting his parishioners, whom he fondly referred to as his "flock".

He probably thought by making a personal visit it would encourage his parishioners, if they needed any encouragement in those days, to continue their regular attendance at church. The early Fifties boasted high church attendances compared to today but were still rather a concern for the clergy, as these were lower than they had been during wartime and lower than cinema attendances. This showed a worrying trend that increasing sections of the population perhaps needed some moral guidance.

When we didn't see Reverend Wheatcroft out and about, he certainly wasn't far from our thoughts; his housekeeper made sure of that, as she kept the neighbourhood up to date with regard to his activities. She naturally came into contact with our neighbours when she was undertaking her routine errands for her employer, Reverend Wheatcroft.

Our vicar was not from around our neighbourhood. He came from a small village in the Eastern county of Cambridgeshire. A burgeoning town like ours in Essex, also in the South-East of England, offered pastures new for someone like him, from out in the sticks. He settled in pretty quickly to our coastal town with its faster pace of life. He had only been our acting vicar for a few years. A relatively large-sized parish like ours to oversee certainly kept him busy.

I understood that clerics could be moved to another diocese by their superiors at the drop of a hat, so I was always afraid that we would lose him and have someone to take his place that was not so approachable and down to earth. He successfully integrated himself into our neighbourhood; this was important, since he was involved in all the main events of a parishioner's life: Christian baptisms (christenings), weddings and funerals.

As well as leading his congregation in worship and prayers, he also presided over the main religious celebrations and festivals of the liturgical year; these included the season of Advent, the celebration of Christmas, the feast of the Epiphany, Lent, and the season of Easter.

Reverend Wheatcroft's main function was to serve people from all walks of life, and endeavour to bring them into the religious fold and strive to keep their faith alive. To this end, he visited various institutions, including schools and hospitals, offering pastoral care and passing on the word of God.

Reverend Wheatcroft took an active part in the parish in which he served. He not only provided spiritual guidance to all where needed but we could also count on him to provide general care and support in the community. Reverend Wheatcroft was a pillar in the community in which he served. He was a hugely respected figure. He quickly earned the respect of our neighbourhood, and certainly mine.

Reverend Wheatcroft served the Anglican Church of England. Ours was a very old church. It was a Norman built church, built on an even older church site, it also boasted a magnificent bell tower, which was erected at a later date, I believe. This church was his place of worship and also of his parishioners. The church is where he also conducted all the important Christian rituals in a person's life: baptisms, weddings and funerals.

Reverend Wheatcroft would stand at the altar at the far end of the east wing of the church to administer the holy sacrament by conducting, or rather celebrating, the Eucharist, or Holy Communion as some people refer to it. A ceremonial table, called the high altar, stands on a raised platform; this area is in the most sacred part of the church, called the sanctuary. In front of the altar is the communion rail (altar-rail), where the congregation kneel to take Holy Communion. The sanctuary is in the chancel, which is where the clergy and choir sit; usually three steps separate the chancel from the central part of the church, the nave, where the congregation sit.

He delivered his sermon from a raised platform surrounded by a stone hexagonal structure, called the pulpit. The pulpit situated on the left, north side of the church, he would have to ascend via a series of curved steps at the side. The pulpit was a special place reserved for him so he could have command from high above over his congregation seated down below in the nave. He must have felt like he was ascending to heaven, which, no doubt, gave him an exalted feeling of power. Reverend Wheatcroft's larger than life extrovert personality was well suited to the role of vicar. He enjoyed playing to an audience, indeed his role required it. He liked nothing better than performing to a full congregation.

* * *

Reverend Wheatcroft resided nearby to our church in an imposing vicarage, which stood in its own grounds. I thought to myself trust the vicar to reside in one of the handsomest, largest, detached houses in town. It had an attractive redbrick exterior, and many small, black, leaded latticed framed windows and larger sash windows. A winding path of crazy paving led up to the large, impressive, old, arched oak panelled front door.

There were so many windows from every angle of that big, old house that I always felt as if someone was watching me every time I made my way up the winding path to the striking front door. I was grateful for the towering sunflowers and tall foxgloves, hollyhocks and lupins standing proudly at either side of the path and in front of the vicarage that masked me partially from view.

The vicarage boasted an enviably large, well-stocked, cottage-style front garden with colourful herbaceous borders. It housed hydrangeas, delphiniums, azaleas (rhododendrons), lobelias, stocks, snapdragons, sweet Williams, pansies and French marigolds; these were just some of the flowers that I could identify.

Other flowers that I was familiar with were lavender, bluebells, tiny forget-me-knots, sweet peas and honeysuckle, when in season. Not forgetting, of course, the ever popular roses. These flowering plants and shrubs provided a colourful display that surrounded the vicarage, extending to the back garden; one could also partially view them from the front, through an arched side gate.

Greeting me near the front porch was a fuchsia bush displaying stunning purplish red bell shaped flowers, which I particularly admired. The porch with its striking architecture was also rather imposing. I particularly liked its decorative, red tiled roof and its patterned, multi-coloured quarry tiled floor. Facing the large, oak panelled front door I felt like I was standing in a confessional box waiting to receive penance for my sins. Its heavy, black iron cast knocker always made me rather reluctant to knock on it! No wonder Reverend Wheatcroft required the services of a housekeeper, and gardener to maintain all that lot for him.

Reverend Wheatcroft's devoted housekeeper Edith, whom he affectionately called "Edie", (Miss Herbert to us children), was a rather anxious looking lady of advancing years. She must have been in her sixties or seventies, at least. She had therefore had many years to be anxious about. This probably accounted for her thin, wiry figure and her worried looking frown, and white hair, which she always tied back in a strict bun. It was therefore not surprising that she greeted me and other children with a stern look on her face. She always watched visiting children rather closely. Either in suspicion, wondering what our business could be with Reverend Wheatcroft or because we were treading on her squeaky clean, highly polished, black and white squared, quarry-tiled hall floor.

She would, "tut-tut", whenever she spotted children in the vicinity expecting us to be guilty of some minor transgression. I always wondered how she managed to undertake all the chores she had to do to maintain this relatively large vicarage, with her slight frame.

She was a diligent worker; however, she also had a tendency to gossip, in what little spare time she had, about the goings-on in the vicarage. Although, with her it was all harmless gossip, as she would never have a bad word to say against Reverend Wheatcroft; she was extremely fond of her master. I expect she was starved of conversation, as she alone undertook all the household duties; a gardener cum handyman took on garden duties and household repairs, but he tended to keep himself to himself. Reverend Wheatcroft meanwhile, preoccupied himself with parochial affairs.

When Reverend Wheatcroft's housekeeper was out and about running errands for him she was bound to come into contact with other gossips in the neighbourhood. People talk and news gets around fast. It's only natural that she, as a devoted housekeeper, would want to boast about the duties that she had to undertake for her master. According to her, she cooked for him and cleaned for him and generally looked after him. She took great pride in her work and looking after her employer.

I understood that she lived within walking distance of the vicarage. I'm sure Reverend Wheatcroft would not have allowed his housekeeper to live-in, despite residing in a large property, which must have boasted several bedrooms. As an unmarried man, Reverend Wheatcroft would not have resided under the same roof with anyone of the opposite sex. Observers would consider such behaviour as amoral and especially the sort of conduct unbecoming of a member of the clergy. Back in those days society was defined by a strict moral code, where this sort of behaviour would have almost certainly provoked gossip!

Reverend Wheatcroft's gardener-cum-handyman, Wilfred, (Mr Peeble to us children), was also of advancing years. He may have been elderly but he was an able gardener and handyman. Despite looking frail and appearing unable to undertake all the physical jobs assigned to him. He always seemed to be busy with something, and could often be seen pottering around the massive vicarage garden.

When he wasn't making good use of his shed busying himself with carrying out a constant stream of minor repairs that needed doing to the house and garden, he would be tending the flowers, mowing the lawn or managing the large vegetable patch at the back. This cultivated plot provided Reverend Wheatcroft with an abundant supply of much needed fruit and vegetables, as it had done during the Second World War, which had ended just over five years previously.

The coalition government had encouraged the population to 'Dig for Victory' and 'Grow Your Own Vegetables' along with fruit, in their gardens. Or if they didn't have a domestic garden, on a public allotment, of which there were many. Even after the war, people were encouraged to grow their own produce because of the food shortages.

Home-grown vegetables and fruit helped to supplement Reverend Wheatcroft's meals, particularly during the long period of food rationing both during the war and after. Rationing lasted right up until 4th July, 1954, when meat, including bacon was the last food item to go off ration, much to Reverend Wheatcroft's delight!

Despite requiring the services of a domestic housekeeper and a gardener-cum-handyman, Reverend Wheatcroft was very agile and sprightly for his age. He too, looked elderly, to me; to a mere child he looked as if he was in his seventies, at least! However, considering that clergymen can carry on working, like judges, until the age of seventy or just beyond that age, on my reckoning he must have been in his late sixties. His agility must have been due to undertaking all those tasks for the church, which his occupation demanded. This is probably why he didn't have time to attend to the housekeeping and gardening chores; he had an able pair of helpers to carry out these functions for him.

The only physical disability that appeared to afflict him was occasional bouts of rheumatism and arthritis, which he said: "rather annoyingly plays up from time to time". He also appeared to suffer from a slight hearing impairment, which meant he often used to ask parishioners to repeat what they had said to him. His housekeeper, Miss Herbert said she often had to repeat things to him because he would refuse to wear his hearing aid in the vicarage.

Reverend Wheatcroft probably found hearing aids rather irksome to wear, as in those days these required a battery box strapped to the body with a microphone amplifier attached by a wire from the box to the ear. However, there were developments to hearing aids in the United States in the early Fifties with the new transistor type.

American Physicists, William Bradford Shockley, John Bardeen and Walter Houser Brattain invented the transistor in 1947 whilst working at Bell Laboratories in the United States. They received the Nobel Prize in Physics in 1956 for their joint work on the transistor. Their important discovery revolutionised hearing aid technology and electronics in general.

The transistor hearing aid was the first commercial product to use transistors. This new type of hearing aid became more widely available in 1953, after their introduction onto the market in 1952. These transistor hearing aids were smaller and less cumbersome than their predecessors, the vacuum tube hearing aids, and more effective. The even smaller and more discreet behind the ear hearing aid was introduced later on, in the second half of the decade; Reverend Wheatcroft didn't have long to wait to benefit from this technological development.

Reverend Wheatcroft had a thin, wiry frame which his tallness helped to accentuate. He was grateful though, for that spindly frame of his, disguising, what he (and his housekeeper) called his, "healthy appetite", but what some would call overindulgence.

Being fairly tall he had an awkward gait. He had developed a gibbosity, a slightly humped back. It was probably all that stooping that he had to do in order to gain admittance through the old, arched church doors and its internal doors, which were fairly low; this was due to the population being shorter in height centuries ago when the church, like other churches, was originally built. Having to constantly stoop his head down due to his tallness in order to hear what his parishioners were saying to him, being slightly deaf, probably also caused his back to be bent.

* * *

Reverend Wheatcroft's attire gave an indication as to his profession. He always dressed in black. He would often be in full dress, which consisted of a long, loose black gown called a cassock (an ankle-length garment) worn with a stiff upright collar.

If he was conducting church services he would be required to wear official ceremonial robes. These are stored in the church vestry (sacristy). Ceremonial robes consist of liturgical garments called vestments, worn by members of the clergy. One such garment is a shorter knee-length, loose smock-styled white gown called a surplice, which has wide, billowing sleeves. Reverend Wheatcroft would wear this over the black cassock, usually with an

'English' stole, which hangs around the neck and down each side of the body like a scarf, usually called a tippet or scarf; it is the length of the surplice and is black in colour.

When Reverend Wheatcroft was conducting religious ceremonies, such as the Eucharist (Communion), he would wear a different vestment, called an alb; this is a loose, white, ankle-length tunic, gathered in at the waist with a cincture (a white or coloured rope belt). Over that he would wear a white circular garment (like a poncho) called a chasuble, which is a loose, sleeveless, ornate outer garment. A bright, plain coloured or white (dependent on the season in the church's liturgical year), longer, slim, silk cloth called a stole, hung loosely around his neck and down each side of his body, underneath the chasuble.

At home in the vicarage or sometimes when Reverend Wheatcroft was out and about in the neighbourhood performing his parochial duties, he would wear a formal looking, sombre black suit. This consisted of a sort of tailcoat, called a frock coat, (which was quite common in the Forties, as a professional form of attire), and underneath, a matching high-necked waistcoat and slim trousers.

His clothes always looked a little dishevelled; the white cuffs of his shirt would often be on show well below the sleeves of his suited jacket, looking rather unseemly. Much to his housekeeper's annoyance, so I heard. His formal, traditional clothing was supposed to signify his important role in society; however, physical appearances were of the least importance to him. According to his philosophy, it's what's on the inside that counts.

The dead giveaway to his profession was, of course, that distinctive stiff starched, white, high-necked clerical collar, or to give it it's popular title, a 'dog collar', which was always on show around his neck. He would also wear black leather lace-up ankle boots, which would squeak when he walked on the hard quarry, terracotta-tiled floor of the church.

I often thought he looked a funny figure in that cassock he wore for church, especially when there was a strong wind blowing outside, which whirled the flowing gown around his ankles. I would watch as the wind gathered speed blowing up his cassock creating a funnel shape like a tornado, as he hurried off after a church service along the main church path leading though the lychgate (lichgate) and out of the churchyard.

He would often joke to us children about the strange garment he had to wear, calling it his "fancy dress!" He also told us that wearing the, "frock", as he sometimes referred to it, created its own problems, as it: "plays havoc with my bicycle, getting caught up in the wheel spokes." So he would often have to resort to wearing his black suit when out and about.

Reverend Wheatcroft looked such a comical sight riding his bicycle. It became a rather haphazard affair. Before mounting that rickety old bicycle of his, he would first have to fit those fiddly cycle clips around his trouser legs. His cycle would then wobble as he kept one hand only on the handlebars to steer it, whilst with the other hand he bid good morning or good afternoon to parishioners he saw in the street or farewell to those who he had just spoken with or visited. His loud, cheery laughter would be trailing behind him as he pedalled slowly up the road. He would then make the rather perilous journey out of our street, first making it to the corner, pedalling slowly, before finally disappearing out of sight!

* * *

I liked Reverend Wheatcroft's cheerfulness and his friendly face. He always greeted everyone he met with an almost permanent, beaming grin on those long, thin lips of his. While those twinkling blue eyes under that receding white hairline gave a hint of his sense of fun underneath those wire-rimmed, archetypical owl-shaped spectacles (probably pre-NHS National Health Service), which pinched his thin, aquiline nose. The tired bags under his eyes appeared more prominent, magnified as they were, through those spectacles he wore.

He had a laugh that resonated. I found it rather surprising, considering his scrawny size, that he had the lung capacity to bellow out such a deep, loud laugh. His booming laughter was audible enough to be heard several doors down the street!

Richard, who was around my age and lived next door to me, was always able to cause Reverend Wheatcroft to throw his head back with laughter. (I have included Richard in Volume II of my character studies of some of the interesting youngsters who lived in the street where I grew up.) Reverend Wheatcroft found Richard's boisterous behaviour and rather flippant comments, comical.

Every time Richard's mother attempted to castigate Richard, Reverend Wheatcroft would step in and say there was no need for her to apologise on behalf of her son: "I need some light-heartedness brought to the proceedings" he would say. He would justify Richard's behaviour by saying, "That's Richard's saving grace: he always manages to make me laugh!" Adding: "I've passed many an entertaining hour in the company of young Richard. It makes for some amusing anecdotes over the dining table with my peers, I can tell you!" And with that, he would laugh out loud again, as he conjured up the scene.

Reverend Wheatcroft possessed a great sense of humour. He enjoyed reading the witty, irreverent, satirical and topical '*Punch*' with its groundbreaking cartoons; this weekly magazine was on a par with his humour. He also enjoyed the popular pictorial, periodical magazine, '*John Bull*', which had some great illustrations. He was also a fan of '*Giles*' humorous, topical cartoons, (according to his housekeeper), depicted in the national newspaper, the '*Daily Express*', and also compiled into annuals.

I, along with others, found his wicked sense of humour and jovial manner rather surprising for a man of the cloth with a serious vocation. But I suppose he would argue that it made him more human and thus more approachable to his flock. His attempts to fit in to the community were successful. He thought rightly so, that a sense of humour would help to ingratiate himself with the locals.

Reverend Wheatcroft was a maverick in his role of vicar, and in his behaviour and habits. Understandably, the old stalwarts amongst his congregation did not always appreciate his rather unconventional approach to his ecclesiastical duties.

The mainly traditional, staunchly conservative congregation, however, tolerated Reverend Wheatcroft's liberal-minded approach to the church and its teachings; he did it in such a way so as not to offend. He delivered his religious instruction in a more light-hearted fashion with the injection of a little humour, without being too dogmatic. In this way his rather unorthodox methods did not pose a threat to the status quo.

He was sharp-witted and possessed a dry sense of humour, which was often lost on some of the more slow-witted of his parishioners. Or on the killjoys amongst them, who were usually the older members of his flock, and in particular, the women. They, like several of my neighbours, Mrs Green, the church flower organiser, and the elderly landladies, Mrs Trenchard and Mrs Starling, (all of whom were the local gossips), were too stuck in their ways to see the funny side in anything, least of all such a serious topic as religion and the Church. Reverend Wheatcroft would just humour them, as best he could.

Reverend Wheatcroft's critics couldn't complain justly, as by and large, he possessed many of the character traits that were ideal for a man of the cloth. Reverend Wheatcroft was unflinching when it came to his commitment to his parochial duties. Besides, he was by now, too old in the tooth to change his ways, a fact that his housekeeper was well aware, much to her irritation. She had often remarked that she had been frustrated in her attempts to change his habits to conform to how she wished to run his household.

In his defence, he would probably declare that a good dose of humour and light-heartedness was what he also personally needed. Possessing himself a sense of humour and being in good cheer helped him to deal with all the trials and tribulations created by the parochial duties and pastoral work he had to undertake in the course of his service to God and to the community at large.

He carried out his pastoral duties in good humour; there were however, often times when he had to display a more solemn mood. I can remember him consoling parishioners during the time of national mourning in February, 1952, when King George the Sixth died, on 6th February. Also, for the national mourning of Queen Mary, the mother of King George the Sixth and wife of the former King George the Fifth, when she died on 24th March, 1953. I can also recall Reverend Wheatcroft celebrating with his parishioners in happier times. This was in the run-up to Queen Elizabeth's Coronation, and on the day itself, on 2nd June, 1953.

Reverend Wheatcroft possessed the perfect temperament to serve parishioners as their pastor. He was highly attuned to the needs of his congregation, and was always ready to listen to parishioners' problems with a sympathetic ear and console them with kind words. He was also quick to give his parishioners every encouragement in their personal endeavours by offering heartfelt words of praise. Reverend Wheatcroft possessed in abundance all the necessary gifts required of a man of the cloth. R.

The community could always rely on Reverend Wheatcroft to help out where he could, particularly in times of need. I can recall him rallying support to raise funds for flood victims during the devastating floods to hit our south-east shores at the end of January and beginning of February, in 1953, which claimed many lives in coastal towns, such as Canvey Island in Essex.

He was kind, caring and sensitive to the needs of his flock. When someone received bad news, he commiserated with them and consoled them in their times of trouble and grief. To those who were sick he would visit them and comfort them with kind words. Sometimes, he went beyond the call of duty to look after the needs of his flock. His housekeeper revealed that he even went out of his way to visit one old lady who was sick and lived at the farthest end of our town. According to his housekeeper's account, he would visit her every day to comfort her by reading to her passages from her favourite book.

Reverend Wheatcroft was a good man with a kind heart. He tried to keep everyone's spirits up when they were low or lacking. He would visit his parishioners at any time of day or night, a bit like the family doctor did in those days when he or she did their rounds. Reverend Wheatcroft did it out of a sense of duty; he felt morally bound to fulfil his pastoral obligations. He believed that God had placed him in charge of the spiritual wellbeing of his, "flock", and so it was, "incumbent", which was another one of his favourite words, on him to fulfil this, his sole function in life.

He offered his moral support to those who had served in the Second World War and were still deeply traumatised by their experiences. He extended his support to families who had young male relatives conscripted for their national service or for those returning home after being demobbed. To those young conscripts often left traumatised by what they had seen and been a part of, he also offered his heartfelt sympathy and support.

Some of these conscripts had been on active service during the political unrest in Palestine, which ended in 1948, when Britain terminated its mandate in Palestine. National service conscripts also served in other hot spots around the world. In Malaya the communists waged a guerrilla war in their bid to liberate their country from British colonial rule. The war in Malaya, led to the increase in the length of national service from one year to eighteen months, under the National Service Amendment Act in December, 1948. The Commonwealth armed forces joined the British armed forces in order to suppress the insurgents.

Britain declared a state of emergency in Malaya in June, 1948; this state of emergency ended in 1960. (Malaya became Malaysia in 1963.) Malaya achieved independence from British colonial rule on 31 August, 1957; the British government extended the state of emergency due to the continuation of communist extremism.

Also, in Kenya there was the Mau Mau uprising, (also referred to as the Mau Mau rebellion). The indigenous population of Kenya initiated the revolt in their bid to end British colonial rule and gain their independence. The British government declared a state of emergency in October, 1952 and sent British troops there to suppress the uprising. The state of emergency there lasted throughout the decade and ended in 1960. Kenya achieved its independence on 12th December, 1963.

Other conscripts were on active service in war-torn Korea. The Korean War, started on 25th June, 1950, when communist-backed forces from the North of the country crossed the '38th parallel' border line separating the North of the country from the South. (The 38th parallel (circle of latitude 38 degrees north of the equator) was chosen by the United States of America after the Second World War, as the demarcation line that separates Soviet-controlled North Korea from United States-controlled South Korea.) After the Second World War, in 1948, North Korea was under the leadership of Kim Il-Sung, the premier of the newly elected, Democratic People's Republic of Korea. While in South Korea the newly elected, Republic of Korea, was under the leadership of its first premier Syngman Rhee.

The Korean War ended with an armistice on 27th July, 1953, with no side claiming victory. The Korean Demilitarized Zone (KDZ) was created after the war separating the two countries roughly along the 38th Parallel; each country is heavily militarised on each side of the border. The British Government extended national service from eighteen months to two years in October, 1950, due to the protracted war in Korea.

In Egypt, the Anglo-Egyptian War started in 1951; this led to the end of British military occupation in 1952. However, Britain's refusal to relinquish military control of the strategically important Suez Canal culminated in the Suez War in 1956.

Everyone in our neighbourhood knew of young men who were doing their national service, whether they were acquaintances, friends or relatives. It was a worrying time in particular for those families with close family members: sons, brothers and husbands who were serving abroad.

Reverend Wheatcroft's spiritual beliefs never waned. He was an eternal optimist, always looking on the bright side, even when there appeared no hope on the horizon. One example of this was when he had to maintain parishioners' belief in God when world events, such as the recently ended Second World War, caused people to strongly question their beliefs. Also, post 1945, with the Korean War that erupted on 25th June, 1950.

British soldiers fought alongside soldiers from other countries, as part of the United Nations (UN) forces. Britain became involved in the war, after communist forces from North Korea overran the 38th Parallel border, which separated the Soviet backed North Korea from the United States backed South Korea.

The Battle of the Imjin River (also known as the Battle of Solma-ri), which occurred over three days, on the 23rd, 24th and 25th April, 1951, was the bloodiest battle to take place in the Korean War. It involved British troops, notably the 1st Battalion of the Gloucestershire Regiment who staved off repeated attacks by Chinese forces. Their brave stand resulted in a number of fatalities on their side, with many wounded and captured by enemy forces. (Communist China entered the war in November, 1950, when it believed its border with North Korea was being threatened by advancing United Nations armed forces.)

The Korean War became a seesaw struggle between the Soviet-backed communists in the North of the country and the United States-backed capitalists in the South. Both sides in the war crossed and advanced beyond the 38th parallel dividing line that separated the North from the South, and then retreated, only to advance again and retreat. This seesaw struggle ended in a stalemate, as North and South Korea reverted to how it was before the war: separated roughly along the 38th Parallel border. Both sides reached a ceasefire on 27th July, 1953. The three year war resulted in a shocking number of fatalities on both sides.

This "senseless war", as Reverend Wheatcroft called it, must also have weighed heavily on people's consciences, causing them to question their belief in a God. Especially those people who knew of British soldiers serving in this conflict. (The Korean War is now often referred to as the 'Forgotten War', because it has received very little media attention compared to other wars. In fact, at the time, the United States censored media coverage of the Korean War.) Reverend Wheatcroft's optimism regarding such dark periods in human affairs must have been born from his strong religious beliefs, which, no doubt, helped him in his calling.

* * *

Reverend Wheatcroft's eagerness to serve the Church was always much in evidence. His religious vocation underpinned everything he did; his enthusiasm to serve was admirable. He would encourage welcome and bid farewell to his parishioners with as much enthusiasm as he could muster.

"The flower display in our Church is looking splendid, as usual. I can always count on you, Mrs Green, and your helpers to provide such a wonderful display!"

"What a joyous sound those church bells make, rung by your husband Mr Green and the other bell-ringers!"

(I have included this married couple in this first Volume of my portrayal of some of the interesting characters who lived in the street where I grew up.)

"Ah, how very nice it is to see you at the Service young man, I hope you found my sermon uplifting!"

"Good day to you Mrs Gosling, nice to see you."

"Ah, Mrs Trenchard, I'm so grateful and honoured that you made it to my Service; I trust you are now in much better health than when we last met!"

Mrs Trenchard was another of our local gossips, (whom I have included in this first Volume).

"Thank you so much Mr Wainwright for gracing my Service, and I very much look forward to seeing you at church next week!"

Mr Wainwright was our local Butcher. He always made sure Reverend Wheatcroft got his rationed supply of much loved bacon, reserved especially for him, as it was on ration until 4th July, 1954! Indeed, it was the last food item derationed, along with other meats, as I've already mentioned. Reverend Wheatcroft was also partial to steak and kidney pudding; in fact it was his favourite savoury dish, according to his housekeeper. She also let it be known that he thought her steak and kidney pudding was the best that he had ever tasted! Mr Wainwright, the butcher, kept certain rationed foodstuffs under the counter for his favourite customers, should he run out of supplies, as many shopkeepers had a habit of doing.

Sometimes, Reverend Wheatcroft's enthusiasm for his vocation could be a little overbearing. Reverend Wheatcroft always took it for granted that his visits to his parishioners were welcome! He would often arrive uninvited on his trusted bicycle to call on his unsuspecting parishioners.

Those being paid a visit in this manner were often put out by Reverend Wheatcroft's unexpected visit. They were embarrassed at the state of untidiness in their homes, as they hadn't had a chance to clear up before he descended on them. His untimely visit would also cause them to worry over whether or not they had sufficient supplies in store to provide refreshments for their important but uninvited guest; this was especially the case during the long period of rationing. Naturally, they felt it their duty to serve a man of the cloth, as most mere mortals would. If Reverend Wheatcroft was not going to be spiritually fed at their home, what would he think of them if they did not provide him with sustenance of some kind!

Reverend Wheatcroft would quickly make himself at home in his host's residence by parting the coat-tails of that frock coat he wore, before predictably, slumping down in the most comfortable armchair right by the fireside! He liked to think his host had reserved it especially for a very important person (VIP): him! He would then plump up the cushion and prop it up behind him so that it nestled into the small of his back.

I can recall the time when on one of his home visits he sat down and narrowly missed Fudge, Richard's little cairn terrier, who thankfully, moved out of the way of his outstretched legs in time to avoid an unintentional kick! I didn't blame Fudge for growling in protest at an impostor removing him from his prominent place by the fireside.

Despite Reverend Wheatcroft's forwardness, which was sometimes unwelcome, he was zealous and hard-working. He had the energy and the physical stamina of a man half his age. These qualities came in useful when having to manage the rather Herculean tasks he had to undertake in our relatively large parish.

His main duties consisted of providing spiritual guidance, conducting church services, teaching the scriptures and delivering sermons. He not only had to look after the spiritual welfare of his flock but also had to manage the church's parochial affairs. This also included overseeing the constant upkeep of our church.

Our church, like any others, was in need of constant maintenance to ensure that it was in a good state of repair. This called upon Reverend Wheatcroft's expertise in helping to raise church funds. He put his verbal and his written skills in particular, to good use to encourage benefactors to contribute generously in order to pay for the substantial cost of church repairs. I remember this included funding for the recasting of two of the ancient bells and rehanging them in the tower.

Reverend Wheatcroft also had to deal with emergencies, such as a constant leaking church roof and the havoc it reaped in the way of damage to the church, namely due to the damp it caused. Being a large church, no sooner than one repair had been successfully undertaken another job needed doing in its place. Reverend Wheatcroft would have to oversee all the work that required attention, stage by stage, which must have given him a few headaches and sleepless nights. Though he could call upon the Parochial Church Council (PCC), which is the executive committee of the Church of England. This body consists of the clergy, churchwardens and those representing the laity, that is, laypersons in the community. But of course, he was the public face and thus viewed by many as being ultimately responsible.

He also had the weighty responsibility of how best to keep his congregation engaged enough to maintain the dwindling numbers attending church. But Reverend Wheatcroft cheerfully took it all in his stride, his motto being, "God's work is never done".

What Reverend Wheatcroft possessed in physical stamina he matched in mental prowess. He possessed a very sharp and alert mind, which he required in order to keep on top of all his duties. He was keen on completing the daily crossword in 'The Daily Telegraph' newspaper, according to his housekeeper; she boasted that he could often complete the crossword in one sitting! That is, whenever time allowed; his parochial and pastoral duties didn't allow him much spare time. Indeed, nothing interfered with his religious calling except for a few extracurricular activities: books, of course, being the main one, and completing the newspaper's crossword. As for his other interests, he successfully managed to combine them with his church commitments.

He was extremely knowledgeable and well informed. His favoured newspapers were the broadsheets, as oppose to the tabloids. His housekeeper, keen to let others know once again, how intelligent her master was, informed them that he read 'The Daily Telegraph', 'The Times' and 'The Observer'. She also commented that he was "always using big words." I can vouch for that: he invariably used big words in conversation. I recall him commenting on the weather with a parishioner: "We have had particularly inclement weather recently", he said.

I knew he could consult reference books, such as the 'Oxford English Dictionary' and 'Roget's Thesaurus', for a little help; he could look up the meaning of a difficult word, or search for a synonym, in order to complete his crossword or for writing his sermons. I had seen well-thumbed copies of each in his study at the vicarage.

I heard, again from his housekeeper, that he always had a satisfied grin on his face and would sigh with pleasure, when he had managed to complete the crossword for that day. I think it must have helped him to sharpen his mental faculties, as did his fondness for playing chess.

According to his housekeeper he was an ardent chess player. He played chess with other clerics who visited him at the vicarage to presumably discuss parochial business.

He owned a superb chess set that consisted of large, carved wood pieces, which would be on permanent display, set out on a board in his study, which I had had the pleasure of seeing. Reverend Wheatcroft and his opponent would tantalizingly leave a game of chess halfway through, according to his housekeeper, although she never used the word 'tantalizingly'. They would continue with their chess moves at a later date. His housekeeper also claimed that he didn't like anyone to interrupt him when he was in the middle of a game of chess. According to her, he also used to practice strategic moves (of course, she didn't use the word 'strategic moves').by playing against himself, when he didn't have an opponent to play against.

When Jeremy, our local grammar schoolboy who lived a few doors down from me, started to play chess, Reverend Wheatcroft would regularly challenge him to a game. (I have included Jeremy in Volume II of my character portrayals of some of the intriguing youngsters who lived in the street where I grew up.)

Reverend Wheatcroft had a highly competitive streak. I don't know who ended up becoming the master of those chess games, as I could not always believe Jeremy when he boasted that he had won playing Reverend Wheatcroft at a game of chess. Reverend Wheatcroft treated chess as if it was an elitist game. He disappointedly, behaved like Jeremy in this respect; he also never challenged me to a game of chess

Jeremy boasted that the rules of chess were quite complicated. It requires several skills. According to him, the game not only requires a high intellect, but apparently, having a good memory also helps. The game of chess involves many game strategies and tactics. Players need to be able to foresee and thus plan in advance all the possible positions to make with their pieces. This requires at the same time, the ability to calculate their opponent's moves, in order to capture their opponent's pieces, with the ultimate goal of setting up a checkmate.

Playing chess must have done wonders for training Reverend Wheatcroft's brain. All the practice made his mind razor-sharp and possibly helped him with his sometimes, failing memory. I think he viewed chess as an intellectual exercise and enjoyed it as mental stimulation for the brain.

Despite possessing an alert brain, Reverend Wheatcroft could be rather absentminded, which he said was due to the nature of his job. He blamed the rigours and stresses of the post he had taken on, which included him having to remember the names and faces of his many parishioners; he was never very good at this, not to mention remembering important dates in his bulging diary.

I think his absentmindedness was also due to his advancing age. His memory, he admitted, was not as alert as it once was. He was often forgetting his sermon notes and had to make a mad dash over to the nearby vicarage for them. But strangely, he never seemed to forget when it was time for luncheon, tea or dinner, or when he had an invitation to partake in food and drink. His housekeeper was keen to report that he was never late when he knew she had prepared for his dinner his favourite: steak and kidney pudding!

* * *

Reverend Wheatcroft had few vices, one of which was gluttony. He would deny though, that he indulged in gluttony. Gluttony was one of the seven deadly sins that the medieval writer Geoffrey Chaucer so perceptively described in, 'The Prologue to the Canterbury Tales' and in 'The Canterbury Tales' themselves. Both written in the late fourteenth century, these character portrayals describe the characters of a motley group of pilgrims on their journey to the religious shrine of Thomas a' Becket, at Canterbury Cathedral. Ironically, it was particularly the religious characters in these works of Chaucer who indulged in sin, and the religious Pardoner and Monk (among other characters), who were guilty of gluttony.

I was surprised that Reverend Wheatcroft's greedy excesses and indulgence didn't show physically in a corpulent figure like Chaucer's description of the Monk. Reverend Wheatcroft's love of food and the pleasure he derived from eating were well-known in the neighbourhood, and probably extended elsewhere. He could always rely on his large circle of friends and extended family members (I understand he had several cousins) living abroad to supply him with regular food parcels to supplement his rations. His love of food was a weakness in his character that he was unable to overcome.

Reverend Wheatcroft had a good excuse for indulging in one of his pleasures, eating; his vocation required that he be a polite host or guest, which meant he was obliged to partake in any food and drink as part of the religious celebrations or offered him by his parishioners. He would indulge himself whenever the opportunity presented itself, which in his capacity as the local vicar was often.

He had all the important church events in the liturgical calendar to preside over, which invariably include a feast of celebratory eating and drinking. There were the Easter celebrations (not of course, during Lent, a period of fasting before Easter), and also the celebration of Christmas. There was also the Harvest Festival in the autumn. Not to mention all the bazaars, summer fetes, fairs and garden parties held throughout the year in the church hall or the vicarage (since it boasted the largest garden). He had to officiate at these functions and always ensured that he stayed around to, as he put it: "sample the food and drink that parishioners had gone to so much trouble to make and prepare."

I heard you could always spot Reverend Wheatcroft at the large trestle table laid out for afternoon tea, either in the church hall or on the village green, depending on the weather. He would be the first one to arrive to take first pick from the huge spread laid on by the WI ladies.

The spread would invariably be a cream tea, consisting of daintily cut, triangular-shaped sandwiches with the crusts cut off; these contained a variety of fillings: thinly sliced cucumber, egg and cress, meat, such as ham and mustard, or fish, such as salmon or tuna, and cheese and pickle. Other savouries would include pork pies, sausage rolls and scotch eggs. There would, of course, be scones served with the traditional clotted cream and preserves (jam). An assortment of pastries, such as individual tarts or a large tart would also be on offer: lemon tart, egg custard tart or my favourite, Bakewell tart. Finally, there would be a selection of cakes or, a large fruit cake or sponge sandwich: a vanilla sponge sandwiched with jam or a chocolate sponge sandwiched with chocolate buttercream.

Reverend Wheatcroft was in his element standing at the tea table eating afternoon tea, with a plate of food in one hand and a cup of tea in the other, whilst indulging in a post-mortem of the finer points of the cricket match with the other players. Naturally, the women made sure that his cup always runeth over by ensuring that it was never empty. They were always at the ready to replenish his cup and refill his plate with tasty fare.

I can recall him on many occasions standing beside the long trestle table in the church hall or in the vicarage garden, which would be groaning under the weight of food, (especially when rationing was over), while he conducted conversations with parishioners. He had a habit of doing this just so that he was nearby and could, at the same time, help himself to all the edible goodies on offer. I can particularly recall him tucking into a few of his favourite savouries: scotch eggs, sausage rolls and pork pies!

He also had his many parishioners to visit who would, more often than not, invite him to a cup of tea and whatever they had in the way of food, such as a piece of homemade cake. They would see it as there moral obligation to offer the vicar some recompense; forgetting of course, or ignorant of the fact, that members of the clergy receive a stipend from their dioceses. Parishioners were only too grateful for his visit, or at least felt honoured to be visited by a man of the cloth, so felt duty bound to offer him something in the way of refreshments, which was the very least they could do.

It was the same with the family doctor; patients would supply them with anything they had to hand, some vegetables or fruit from the garden, eggs, fish, meat, etcetera. This would be in lieu of payment if they couldn't afford to pay and the doctor was agreeable. This happened both before the inception of the National Health Service and after, when patients had not got out of the habit of offering their doctor some form of recompense, despite doctors' receiving by then, a salary from the State.

Parishioners would treat Reverend Wheatcroft like a V.I.P. when they invited him for tea, often at his own invitation! I remember when Reverend Wheatcroft invited himself to Richard's parent's house; I happened to be visiting him that afternoon. I only witnessed the preparations for Reverend Wheatcroft's impending visit, as unfortunately, I wasn't invited to stay at Richard's. With all the fuss made on that day, anyone would have thought royalty was coming! And even if they were, I would not treat them any differently! But then, I suppose, his worship the Reverend Ernest Wheatcroft was aware that in the eyes of his parishioners he was special! He was the closest person they were likely to meet of high rank and social standing.

The preparations at Richard's parent's house mirrored those in other parishioners' homes when they knew of an impending visit by their vicar. They would honour Reverend Wheatcroft by entertaining him in the best room in the home. This would be the front room or 'sitting' room', as it was also called, or 'lounge', as my mother, who considered herself middle class, preferred to call it. They really rolled out the red carpet for their very important guest! Richard's mother certainly looked frazzled, as she frantically tried to ensure that everything ran to order, in time for Reverend Wheatcroft's impending visit. Anyone would have thought he was a drill sergeant about to come and inspect barracks!

The best linen, white tablecloth and napkins would surface from the side cabinet drawer and the best crockery laid out on the table. Only on very special occasions, such as the local vicar visiting, did a parishioners' best china tea set see the light of day! They would present Reverend Wheatcroft with fragile, white bone china teacups, saucers and matching side plates, patterned with dainty, small, coloured flowers and all edged in gold leaf. How on earth they expected Reverend Wheatcroft to grip his arthritic fingers around those fiddly, delicate handles was anyone's guess! Those tiny teacups were like something out of a doll's tea party! Having to navigate his fingers round those cups without being clumsy was a feat in itself.

Naturally, Reverend Wheatcroft had the best in the way of food offered to him, in spite of when food rationing was still in force. I can recall Richard craftily taking a peek inside the sandwiches that his mother asked him to carry on a large plate into the front room. It was no surprise to him that he spied ham; parishioners reserved only the best for their vicar. All the rest of us usually got tinned Spam!

Where Spam got its name is still debatable. It was possibly a contraction of 'spiced ham' 'spare meat', or 'shoulders of pork and ham'. Another possibility was that SPAM, as it's named on the tin, was an acronym for 'Specially Processed' or 'Pressed' American Meat'.

This popular, precooked and processed tinned meat, which consists mainly of pork shoulder with a small amount of ham (cured hind leg, as oppose to shoulder) in it, was a cheaper meat alternative. Britain imported it from the United States at the time when rationing of other meat in Britain during, and after the war, was still in force.

So by offering Reverend Wheatcroft ham, Richard's mother really had pushed the boat out! By all accounts, Reverend

Wheatcroft was very impressed with the efforts Richard's mother had gone to and laid on the compliments thick and fast.

It was the same with the ladies at the Women's Institute, the WI; Reverend Wheatcroft would always flatter them with compliments on their baking accomplishments. Flattery flowed so easily from Reverend Wheatcroft's lips though, compared to the hard work those WI ladies had to endure to prepare the delicious spreads they laid on in the church hall or in the vicarage garden.

Reverend Wheatcroft would raise his hands and let out a pleasurable sigh while he feasted his eyes on the trestle table laden with food, as if he was conducting one of his sermons to his congregation! I always thought he had been saving himself up for these feasts all day! He would then press his bony, bent arthritic finger up to his lips while he surveyed the edible goodies, thinking of what he could come up with in the way of encouraging compliments. He was very skilled at dishing out compliments. "Ah! What a delightful tea!" "What a delectable feast!" "A spread fit for a King!"

When he referred to rationed foodstuffs, he would exclaim: "I must say I'm very impressed! It's quite a remarkable feat and requires considerable imagination to stretch what resources we currently have to make do with."

Reverend Wheatcroft had a habit of piling on the compliments when he was benefiting in some way. "Do you know, ladies, these sandwiches really do taste delicious!" His flattery always seemed to have the desired effect, as the ladies of the WI, just like his parishioners, were completely taken in. "Here, help yourself Reverend Wheatcroft", they would reply, holding out a plate of food for him.

Reverend Wheatcroft would also appeal to the WI ladies pride in their baking by making an indirect request for a sample of their baking.

"Do you know, I'm wondering if those scones taste as scrumptious as they look?" The ladies of the WI would fall for the bait every time! "Oh, forgive my manners Reverend Wheatcroft, please try one!" Eager to please and in the hope of yet more compliments, the ladies would offer him another morsel to eat, such as a slice of cake, to which his reply was usually: "I wouldn't say no!"

Reverend Wheatcroft had a sweet tooth and was extremely fond of cake. His favourite was a vanilla sponge sandwich, consisting of two layers of sponge sandwiched together with a jam filling, more commonly known as a jam sponge sandwich, Victoria sponge or Victoria sandwich. I suppose, being somewhat deprived of this particular cake when butter and sugar, and indeed eggs were rationed, made him more partial to this butter and sugar rich cake. When all the ingredients were available, his housekeeper was able to indulge him, as were the ladies of the WI at their WI teas held in the church hall or vicarage garden for all the church fetes and fairs.

I would listen to Reverend Wheatcroft singing his praises of the WI women's' baking skills, and in particular, for their jam sponge sandwich. "Ah, the piece de resistance, that Victoria sponge, which takes pride of place in the middle of the table, looks irresistible!"

Typically, the ladies would then offer him a very generous wedge of the jam sponge, which he was only too keen to take off their hands. I would observe him in amusement as he squeezed the sponge sandwich gently between his forefinger and thumb to test for sponginess! Then he would say, "I congratulate you, top marks Mrs…" Waiting for the recipient to fill him in on her name, as he was never any good at remembering names, before he would continue:

"You've excelled yourself; this sponge really is a worthy effort! It is truly delectable! I don't think Edie, my housekeeper has managed yet to make her sponge as light and airy in texture as this, but don't tell her I said so!" He would then grin from ear to ear, like a mischievous schoolboy in possession of a secret, while the ladies of the WI would blush with pride at their achievement.

Reverend Wheatcroft always had plenty of excuses for his overindulgence. He would blame his parishioners for spoiling him with food and drink on his regular home visits, or when served by the ladies of the WI. Every time when food and drink was in the offering he would willingly oblige, as if he was doing his parishioners or the ladies of the WI a favour. "You needn't have gone to so much trouble, but now that you have, it would be rude of me to refuse" was his oft used retort. Reverend Wheatcroft was as cunning as a fox!

His other excuse for eating at every opportunity offered to him, was that he was underfed due to his busy schedule, which he said, didn't allow him time to partake in a proper meal. Although his conscientious housekeeper-cum-cook, Miss Herbert, would beg to differ!

"Do you know, Mrs Sims, (he usually ensured that he got the name right if he was visiting a parishioner in their home), I've worked up quite an appetite with all the duties I've had to attend to today."

Or, his retort would be: "You'll have to excuse my hearty appetite dear lady (if he really couldn't remember her name, or 'sir' if it was a gentleman), but this is the first opportunity I've had to eat since having a hurried breakfast this morning and barely time for a quick bite to eat at luncheon!"

He always reminded me of a ravenous bird the way he watched eagle-eyed, the person passing around the plate, which held some delicious delicacy. Due to deference he would usually be their first port of call. I found his bird-like gestures quite amusing. Like the way he would move forward and outstretch his bony, talon-like fingers towards plates of daintily cut sandwiches and greedily help himself to several sandwiches, from both plates! He behaved like a ravenous, sharp-eyed eagle.

He would greedily eye and weigh up the plate of scones, another favourite of his, which the WI ladies eagerly held in front of him, as if he was an architect assessing structures! "Those sultana scones have certainly risen to the occasion, they're leaning high like the leaning Tower of Pisa!" Typically, he would then select the biggest scone and then help himself to a generous portion of butter from the butter dish. He conveniently chose to forget when butter was on ration! He would then bite into the fat scone keeping the WI ladies anxiously waiting for his verdict, while he slowly savoured it ... managing to finally exclaim, in-between mouthfuls, "Umm…" Then he would be gushing in his praise:

"This scone is one of the best I've ever tasted and, I've sampled quite a few in my time. You ladies have done yourselves proud."

He was trying to butter the WI ladies up! He succeeded! They would look flushed with their achievement in pleasing the vicar and would fall over themselves in their eagerness to attend to his dietary needs by offering him more edible delights and tea. To which his quick reply was always: "Thank you.", and, "Yes please, I'd love another cup."

Reverend Wheatcroft liked nothing better than partaking in another of his favourite pastimes, which was drinking tea. He would often hold out his teacup to whoever was the host or hosts for them to replenish it. Reverend Wheatcroft would drink copious amounts of tea when it came off ration in 1952, in common with the nation whose favourite drink back in the fifties was tea, as it was and still is mine.

The Tetley tea company introduced the first teabag in Britain in 1953. But as with anything new and innovative, I think it took quite a while to catch on, as people were used to the old and trusted method of straining the tea leaves through a tea strainer.

I heard Reverend Wheatcroft was also rather partial to Camp Coffee essence, a coffee-flavoured syrupy concoction made mainly from the essence of chicory leaves. This drink was particularly popular with Scottish soldiers serving in India in the era of the British Empire. (The label on the famous bottle depicts a Scottish soldier and an Indian Sikh.) According to Reverend Wheatcroft's housekeeper, he would have his camp coffee topped up with a saucepan of gently heated milk. However, I did hear a rumour, no doubt circulated by his landlady, that he had developed a strong liking for instant (soluble) coffee.

Instant coffee was first universally popular with the United States military during the Second World War. It started to become more popular in Britain in the mid-Fifties with well-known brands, such as Nescafe (first manufactured in Britain in 1939), and later, Maxwell House, which improved its manufacturing processes. The Maxwell House brand of instant coffee went on sale in Britain in 1954. But instant coffee was an acquired taste, and of course, more expensive than the nation's favourite tipple, tea.

Reverend Wheatcroft certainly wasn't a teetotaller by any stretch of the imagination; not like one of our neighbours, Miss Marsden, who was renowned for being a teetotaller. (I have included a study of this intriguing character in Volume III.) He made no secret about his liking for alcoholic beverages: a good malt whisky, claret and port, in particular. However, luxuries, such as alcohol, although never rationed, along with tobacco, were expensive and difficult to obtain. Reverend Wheatcroft also enjoyed smoking a pipe.

Reverend Wheatcroft's liking for drink was well-known in the neighbourhood. Parishioners though, would usually offer him sherry, which was the more popular, and of course, affordable drink for the masses; it apparently, always went down well with him. He also enjoyed a beer, whether it be light ale, bitter or stout, if he was offered it; he said it always "hit the spot" in quenching his thirst, particularly in hot weather. Sherry was the tipple also preferred by the older parishioners, who were stalwarts when it came to their drinking habits. They would bring sherry out of its hiding place to see the light of day usually only on celebratory occasions.

Unsurprisingly, parishioners always seemed to have something to celebrate and drink a toast to: birthdays, Christmas and the New Year, being the main annual events. Then of course, there were baptisms (christenings) and weddings. Special events also included the end of the Second World War 'Victory in Europe (VE) Day' celebrations on 8th May, 1945, and the days leading up to Queen Elizabeth the Second's Coronation on 2nd June, 1953. Even a gloomy event, like the national mourning of King George the Sixth, in February, 1952, and his mother Queen Mary, in March, 1953, would provide them with a good excuse to have a drink to assuage their grief.

The Coronation in June, 1953, of course, provided everyone, Reverend Wheatcroft included, the opportunity to really indulge in alcoholic merriment. He was able to indulge to his heart's content with the whole country and beyond our shores, in order to celebrate this auspicious occasion. During this special time there were street parties and other celebrations taking place up and down the country, prior to and including the Coronation Day itself. All of which involved a lot of food and drink.

The special Coronation event gave Reverend Wheatcroft a good excuse to indulge himself; as an important, upstanding member of the community he was a constant figure at these celebrations, partaking of the food and drink offered to him. By all accounts, he got quite tipsy during that time, with all the sherry on offer, not to mention other alcoholic beverages. But then, so did other people, so he was not alone. Most people believed they had cause to be merry, as it was a special time in our country's history, the birth of a new era, the 'New Elizabethan Age'. So Reverend Wheatcroft's slight drunkenness wouldn't have raised many eyebrows.

Naturally, Reverend Wheatcroft reserved his private drinking for the evenings. He defended his drinking by saying that a glass of whisky, claret or port, as an occasional nightcap before he retired to bed, helped him to relax from the rigours and strains that his post as vicar entailed. His housekeeper though, insisted on preparing his night-time cup of cocoa, so she said. Whether he drank it or poured it into a potted plant standing nearby on an occasional table in his study, no one will ever know.

Apparently, Reverend Wheatcroft would enjoy a glass of whisky, claret or port, in the evening after supper, when he had retired to his study. His housekeeper revealed that he would often pair it with a piece of Wensleydale cheese and some savoury biscuits and chutney or some dark chocolate. She said, sometimes he would invite a small gathering of male friends round for a drink. Presumably, he would host a small soiree and share a glass with a male companion or two who would invariably be other church clerics.

His housekeeper also confirmed that he would indulge in a glass of his favourite tipple to help him unwind. I assume this was probably after discussing the rather dry topic of parochial business. Of course, he would enjoy a drink over a "particular taxing game of chess", which he said required, "a little lubrication" to get his, "brain into gear". Although, I thought alcohol had quite the opposite effect!

Reverend Wheatcroft's housekeeper revealed that apart from cake and other sweetmeats, and alcoholic beverages and coffee, Reverend Wheatcroft also had a liking for chocolate and in particular, Bourneville dark chocolate. She said he also liked milk chocolate covered Fry's Turkish Delight with its rose-coloured and flavoured jelly centre. What's more, he had such a sweet tooth that he also had a liking for cubes of Turkish Delight dusted with icing sugar, so she said.

Apparently, Walnut Whip was another favourite of his, with it's whipped vanilla fondant centre contained in that volcanic looking, cone-shaped thick chocolate; not forgetting that added bonus of a half walnut inside, which, if my memory serves me, was later moved on top. Of course, Reverend Wheatcroft was able to indulge himself when chocolate was more readily available, after it had been derationed along with sweets, on 5th February, 1953.

According to Reverend Wheatcroft's housekeeper who naturally gossiped with some of the women folk, in an attempt to restrict his intake of chocolate when it was on ration he would hide it in certain places around the vicarage; he found the temptation just too much. Luxury beverages, such as whisky, claret and port although never rationed, a point I made earlier, were obviously in short supply and thus were very difficult to obtain. So he would often secrete these in a secret hiding place too.

It was the same with Lent. Apparently, Reverend Wheatcroft found it extremely difficult to forgo chocolate during this special time in the Christian liturgical calendar. This is from Ash Wednesday to the day before Easter Sunday, where for forty days followers (following in the footsteps of Jesus' Forty Day fast in the wilderness), are required to, among other things, (such as fasting, prayer and confession), abstain from eating and drinking something that they derive pleasure from. In Reverend Wheatcroft's case, this included whisky, claret, port and chocolate, particularly when these luxury goods were more available.

He had to exert strong willpower over this period of abstinence, in order not to yield to temptation. This caused him, once again, to secrete his chocolate and drink around the vicarage, so that it would be harder for him to give in to temptation. But his housekeeper disclosed that by the time Lent had passed and it came to locating the chocolate bar, which was smaller to hide than a bottle, of course, he couldn't remember where he had hidden it, let alone find it, much to his frustration!

* * *

To be fair, gluttony, and indulging in the demon drink now and then were probably Reverend Wheatcroft's only vices. I wasn't aware of any others. Besides, he had many virtues, which I've already touched on, to make up for what he lacked in restraint in his eating and drinking habits. He was an excellent vicar and did the Church a great service by attracting a relatively large congregation considering attendances had been dwindling since the last war.

He tried to make his sermons interesting to the young and old alike, and I think, on the whole, he succeeded. Judging by the large attendance at our local church, parishioners enjoyed listening to his church sermons on Sunday and other special days of worship. These were certainly the highlight of the services for me; Reverend Wheatcroft was worth going to see for his sermons alone.

Reverend Wheatcroft always knew when to be joyous and when to be sombre, according to what service he was relaying. He also, always tried to raise the standard of his sermons so they weren't just old-fashioned and stuffy sermons; he made his sermons interesting by making them topical and often including a humorous anecdote. He was extremely articulate and highly skilled in the art of rhetoric so he was able to appeal to all sorts of people through his sermons. He was even able to capture the attention of the youngest members of his congregation by his humorous and energetic delivery.

Naturally, there were some in his congregation, the old stalwarts, who found his sermons just too uplifting and unconventional; they complained that they thought he went too far, that he should have shown more restraint. Although his critics were quick to condemn him amongst themselves, they wouldn't dare say anything to his face. He got to hear it second-hand. He often said he had learnt to develop over the many years of sermonizing, a thick skin, and to turn the other cheek when necessary.

Reverend Wheatcroft's reply to silence his critics was that in his, "attempts to try to attract the younger ones and keep them engaged", he was aware that at the same time he would, "unfortunately be alienating some of the older members" of his "flock". He said there was always a danger in doing that, and what is more, one couldn't please everyone all of the time. He would do his best to humour his critics in other more subtle ways.

Reverend Wheatcroft had a cunning streak. Sometimes in his sermons he would make subtle remarks with reference to certain members of his congregation but would dress it up in such a way that they weren't aware that he was really referring to them. He was very clever like that. He was skilled in the subtle art of, "getting people on side", which is a cricket term that he was fond of using. He would first beguile them with his charm and pile on the compliments, then make his strategic move and go in for the kill! People said he could charm the birds off the trees.

He had such a way with people that he was able to count on their support for any enterprise that he might be undertaking. He was very adept at getting parishioners to volunteer their services: whether it was to call on their help in fund-raising; carrying out odd jobs around the church, or at the vicarage (when his handyman-cum-gardener was unable to carry out these tasks himself), or to help with other chores and activities. Before they realized it they had agreed to his polite requests. This is one of the drawbacks of being intelligent: they sometimes think the other person is not perceptive enough to see through the subtleties of their deceptive behaviour.

I recall an occasion when Reverend Wheatcroft's cunningness was in full operation. He had invited himself round to Richard's parents for tea. I happened to be present again at the time and stayed on this occasion, so I managed to be a witness to what took place and overheard most of the conversations.

It transpired that Reverend Wheatcroft had an ulterior motive for inviting himself to Richard's parent's home. The reason for his visit, he said, was to discuss Richard's increasing absence from church. Richard no longer attended Sunday school believing he was too old and so started attending the church services with his parents, albeit reluctantly. He had managed to get out of attending several services.

The Church in general was becoming less appealing to youngsters, as the decade wore on, in spite of Reverend Wheatcroft's best efforts. Richard naturally joked, as he had a habit of doing, that he was surprised his absence from church had been noticed, to which Reverend Wheatcroft jokingly replied: "Come, come Richard, nothing much goes unnoticed by me." He gave Richard a knowing smile, while he lifted his teacup slowly up to his lips, all the while training his eyes on Richard, which was another of his little idiosyncrasies.

Reverend Wheatcroft artfully managed to avoid disclosing the main reason for visiting Richard's parent's home until the end of his visit, after he had supped and eaten to his heart's content. Before taking his leave, he hesitated, which was customary for him:

"Ah, I nearly forgot to mention, before I depart", he said: "There was one other thing I have been meaning to discuss with you Mr and Mrs Wheeler.... " He had a convenient habit of forgetfulness and would often pause at the end of a conversation. It was usually his cunning way of pretending that what he was about to add was a mere afterthought, while all along he had cunningly withheld this vital piece of information until the very last. That is, until after he had buttered up his parishioners first.

He typically took his time, pausing, holding that bony finger of his, up to his pursed lips, while he pondered on how he could best broach the subject with Richard's parents. I might have guessed Reverend Wheatcroft had an ulterior motive for his visit! He was just using Richard's non-attendance at church as an excuse, or trying to kill two birds with one stone!

He finally spelled out the real reason for his visit: "I understand Mrs Wheeler that you still have a spare room available, now that your daughter Brenda has moved out with her new husband." As an afterthought, he followed this observation by craftily reminding Richard's parents' that: "I have fond memories of marrying the happy couple in my church, a couple of years ago."

(Due to the general lack of housing it was customary for young, newly married couples to live with either the groom or the bride's parents, usually the bride's parents. If there wasn't enough room, a married couple would be forced to live apart, until they could find suitable accommodation.)

Before Richard's mother had a chance to reply, Reverend Wheatcroft had invited a young man who he said, was: "in dire need of a place to stay." I had spied Reverend Wheatcroft earlier that Sunday morning in church in deep conversation with a rather nervous looking, young man.

Noticing Richard's mother's look of alarm at having a stranger to stay Reverend Wheatcroft then tried to reassure her. He informed her that she: "...wouldn't be put out too much, as it was only a temporary arrangement, that is, until we can find the young man something more permanent."

People often rented out their homes to those in need of a place to stay. Large sections of the population who were expelled or who fled from war-torn Eastern Europe were made homeless during and after the war. Many of these displaced persons and refugees settled in Britain; they also settled in other European countries, and in the United States of America and Canada.

British citizens were also made homeless; their homes were destroyed or made uninhabitable due to bomb damage in the wartime Blitz. Many homes were also badly dilapidated due to age and neglect; these were categorised as slums, but the government had to put their slum clearance programme on the backburner due to the start of the Second World War. People who owned a home needed the spare cash they got from letting out a spare room when times were hard during the war and in the aftermath.

Reverend Wheatcroft went on to explain that this particular person he was trying to help was a young man who had come from overseas, which is why his English was not too good. Apparently, he came from a small village; Reverend Wheatcroft mentioned something about it being in what was once Prussia.

I have since found out that Prussia was a former state of the German Empire and a Kingdom before the monarchy was overthrown and it became a Republic in 1918. After the Second World War, Poland and the Soviet Union divided Prussia into their own territories and thus it ceased to exist. Reverend Wheatcroft was doubtless confident that Richard's parents hadn't heard of the place, and due to their ignorance of such matters they therefore wouldn't ask too many probing, awkward questions.

Reverend Wheatcroft then, with foresight, attempted to allay any fears they may have harboured at having a stranger to stay in their home. He explained: "The details of his background are rather sketchy, but I have it on good faith from a reliable source that he is of good character, so you have nothing to fear, that's why I'm entrusting him to your household Mrs Wheeler."

He then, with great foresight once more, allayed their worries over how they could afford to pay for his upkeep by declaring that they needn't concern themselves with any financial matters, as: "that would all be taken care of so you've no worries on that score Mr and Mrs Wheeler. I'm sure we'll come to some amicable arrangement…" he added.

Now that Reverend Wheatcroft had laid the ground work for his cunning plan, and since he was asking Richard's parents to literally take a stranger into their home, he prayed on their sympathy. He was quick to inform them that the young man in question, like so many others, was a displaced person; the recent war had separated his family. And that like so many others, he had come to this country to live and make a new start for himself.

Reverend Wheatcroft backed his claim up by stating that he was sure that Richard's parents had: "Read all about the poor plight of these displaced people who find themselves, through no fault of their own, in less fortunate circumstances than our own." He added that their plight had been, "well documented in all the newspapers." He made one final plea by appealing to Richard's parents' moral and social conscience: "Many of these refugees, like the young man in question, have come to this country to live, as they have no other place to go. So we have a moral obligation to help out where we can to accommodate them."

Reverend Wheatcroft then went on at length to drive his point home: "And since this young man has come to reside in our neighbourhood, it is incumbent on me to help out a member of my flock in his hour of need. Indeed, it falls on all of us to make him feel welcome and help him to fit into the community. So you would not only be doing me, a huge favour but also the community as a whole Mr and Mrs Wheeler, if you took him under your wing."

Observing that Richard's parents were about to ask him some questions in order to find out more information on the subject, he interjected: "Look, I'll gladly answer any more questions you may have Mr and Mrs Wheeler, when I'm in possession of the full facts myself. For the moment, I'll just leave you in the knowledge that he comes with good credentials; I can vouch for him."

Before Richard's parents had time to respond he finished the conversation with: "That's settled then. Excellent! I'll be in touch soon with regard to arranging a time for him to come to stay." With that he was quick on the mark, standing to his feet and patting out the creases in his trousers, which he had a habit of doing when extricating himself from a chair. He intended making a hasty exit when it suited him!

* * *

The majority of Reverend Wheatcroft's parishioners couldn't compete with him on an intellectual level and he knew this; he was therefore able to use this to his own advantage. Reverend

Wheatcroft was a highly educated and erudite man. I had noticed on our church noticeboard outside the church, displaying the times of the various church services, that he had a special title with letters after his name: 'Reverend Ernest Wheatcroft, MA (Cantab)'. His title looked very impressive. I was always intrigued to know what these letters stood for.

I harboured a secret ambition, which was to have letters after my name, one day. Having a title and letters after his name made him stand out from the usual, 'Tom, Dick and Harry'. It gave him status, as most people just had plain (Mr, Mrs, Miss, or Master (for a boy), with nothing after their name. Having letters after one's name, I thought, was something worth aspiring to.

Most people in our neighbourhood thought it wasn't for the likes of us to aspire to anything, apart from Jeremy that is, being the only youngster in our street to attend the local grammar school. Although, some of our elderly neighbours, understandably thought attending the grammar school had made Jeremy "too big for his boots". Reverend Wheatcroft was different to most people in that respect also, he was very liberal and fair-minded; he believed that we should all aspire to something and should not simply accept our allotted place in life. He often told us youngsters that we would each find our true vocation. He believed that everyone was special.

I think Reverend Wheatcroft expected great things of me, and I wasn't about to let him down, or myself for that matter. He was constantly saying that the world is your oyster. I didn't entirely believe him though. I became increasingly aware while I was growing up that for most, it would be a hard struggle to get on in life and become socially mobile, since there was still a deep class divide in Britain in the Fifties.

The Education Act 1944, (often referred to as the 'Butler Act', named after the Conservative politician and President of the Board of Education 'Rab' Butler, who was responsible for steering the bill through Parliament), would supposedly help to close the class divide; it would provide equal opportunities in education. It provided for free secondary education for all children, regardless of background; it also raised the school leaving age from fourteen to fifteen.

Children of differing abilities would be served by three schools proposed under the tripartite system: grammar, technical and secondary modern. In effect it became a two-tier, bipartite system, as the technical school failed to materialise. The grammar school which offered its pupils a more academic education would provide society with educated elites; this group would enter the professions. The secondary modern, which offered its pupils practical skills, would provide society with unskilled labour, that is, workers with a limited skill set. Pupils who passed the eleven-plus examination obtained a state-funded scholarship to the grammar schools. (Grammar (direct-grant) schools that took fee-paying students still existed; however, these were in a minority.)

The introduction of the state-funded scholarship was to enable pupils from the poorer working classes to have access to a superior education, which the grammar schools offered. The tripartite system was supposed to create a meritocracy. Passing the eleven-plus examination would ensure these select pupils achieved a grammar school place by merit alone (if there was a place available), instead of reliance on their parents' ability to pay. This enabled those from a poorer working class background to achieve by merit and talent alone rather than on class, wealth and privilege. A few token cases however, were not enough to change anything for the masses, it just assimilated those few into the middle classes and thus into an acceptance of the status quo.

While for those of us not fortunate enough to attend the grammar school the future looked dim, as it would take Herculean efforts on our part to climb the social ladder in order to achieve the dizzy heights of success. In the decades that followed, sociological studies have since discovered that the selection system was, (and still is), grossly unfair. These studies have found that many children denied a grammar school education, were in fact, as bright, if not brighter than those children who had been offered a place!

I found out what the letters after Reverend Wheatcroft's name stood for, when he asked me to stop off at the vicarage next time I was passing for a book he said he intended to lend me. I think he viewed me, and perhaps Richard, as a challenge, or saw potential in us (I like to think the latter applied to me), and had taken it upon himself, as a personal crusade to educate us in worldly matters. He had taken us under his wing, thinking that we were a worthy cause, or perhaps lost sheep that needed guidance, (the latter probably applied to Richard and that other displaced, young man). He knew that, unlike Richard, I was interested in reading and books. I thought he probably wanted to lend me a boring book on religion!

Reverend Wheatcroft's housekeeper always took her time to answer the vicarage door. I suspect she was busy with her mid-morning chores and seeing to the needs of her master and the likes of me standing knocking on that heavy doorknocker was just an irritant she could have well done without. When she finally opened the door, she peered suspiciously at me, over the top of her round, wire-rimmed spectacles, while I explained the reason for my presence. She paused and then grumbled something under her breath, before finally, and albeit reluctantly, allowing me in over the threshold.

I followed her along the hallway, passing a handsome, impressive, old grandfather clock in the hallway, which rather startled me with its deep tick-tock, echoing the time. She then showed me, once again, rather reluctantly, into Reverend Wheatcroft's study.

I found Reverend Wheatcroft reclining in a comfortable looking, soft, and high back armchair seated by the French windows that opened out into his extensive back garden. Reverend Wheatcroft was wearing his black frock coat with its long coat-tails draped over the sides of the chair; he looked completely relaxed. His legs outstretched, with his feet placed on a small, burgundy-coloured velour upholstered footstool, one booted foot crossed over the other.

All I could hear was the cracking of those black leather ankle boots he was wearing, with every slight movement of his feet. His elbows were resting on the armrests of the chair, with a lit pipe held in one hand, and the other holding an outstretched newspaper, which he was reading intently. Reverend Wheatcroft must have been reading the extensive coverage in the newspaper of the headline news that day.

I can still recall the newspaper's main headline. It was about cricket and England regaining the Ashes after nineteen years, on 19th August, 1953, with the fifth and final test played at the famous England cricket ground, the Oval. The list of star players included Essex-born Trevor Bailey. There was also Alec Bedser, Bill Edrich and Fred Truman. Len Hutton captained the team. Denis Compton was among the players.

Denis Compton was also famous for being the 'Brylcreem Boy'. He was the well-known face of that era with his distinctive, dark, slicked back hair featured on all the advertisements for Brylcreem hair products, advertised exclusively for men. (Before that, during World War Two, members of the men's Royal Air Force (RAF), were known as the original 'Brylcreem Boys' because of their glamorous image helped by their neatly combed, smooth, slicked back, Brylcreemed hairstyles.)

The 1953 Cricket Match must have been a memorable one for Reverend Wheatcroft. He absolutely adored cricket by all accounts. He would converse for ages with parishioners on cricket matches, including those played on the local village green.

I often saw Reverend Wheatcroft in animated conversation with our aptly named neighbour Mr Green, who was one of the church bell-ringers and also a follower of cricket. (I have included Mr Green and his wife in this first volume of my character studies of some of the interesting people who inhabited the street I lived in whilst growing up.)

Reverend Wheatcroft didn't share Mr Green's love of football though, which was the most popular sport back then in Britain, as it is today. Apparently, Reverend Wheatcroft played cricket whilst he was an undergraduate at Cambridge University. And before that, at the public school he attended, which is probably where his interest in cricket stemmed from.

During the cricket season, if there was an important match playing and Reverend Wheatcroft happened to be visiting a parishioner at the time, he would cheekily ask them if they wouldn't mind switching their wireless on so that he could hear the latest scores and fixtures. He was well aware that his parishioners wouldn't deny his wish, as they wouldn't like to refuse a man of the cloth such a simple request.

Reverend Wheatcroft would also delight in organising and taking part, since, as I said, he was very sprightly and agile for his age, the cricket matches for the church fundraising. For him, one of the highlights of these amateur cricket matches were the afternoon teas the ladies of the WI laid on afterwards, which he always looked forward to. He was able to successfully combine his love of cricket with his love of food.

Obviously, I didn't like to disturb Reverend Wheatcroft from reading his newspaper so I stood in silence in his study. While he was engrossed in his newspaper I had time to look around the room. His study possessed that very distinct, musty smell that one usually associates with old books that have collected dust and mildew over the years. The smell of tobacco also filled the room. A plume of smoke rose in the air from the pipe he was smoking intermittently. I had never seen so many books! That is, apart from in our local public lending library. Even Miss Marsden, our bookish, middle-aged neighbour, I'm sure, didn't own nearly as many books.

Sitting in a nearside corner of the room was an attractive but old looking, well used, dark mahogany wood writing bureau. The top half of the bureau consisted of a tall, latticed wood framed and glass windowed bookcase. In it, was housed some of his book collection, which were shelved in three tiers with their leather and cloth spines on display. There was another mahogany wood, one tier bookshelf mounted on the wall, also lined with books. While yet another larger four tier bookshelf stood in another alcove, overflowing with books, which he had also piled on top through lack of space. There were also books lying side by side on the waxed wooden floor surrounding his desk, which reminded me of a row of falling dominoes!

Dominoes were a popular game during the Fifties, in which players match together distinctive marked blocks of wood or plastic, called dominoes. These are small, flat, oblong pieces 'tiles' divided into two halves; each half is either blank or marked with a number of dots 'pips'. The player places the dominoes down, side by side or edge to edge in order to form a configuration.

Many of Reverend Wheatcroft's books looked old and in a fragile state, some had broken spines. These books didn't lend themselves to being handled, in case they fell apart in one's hands. So I could quite understand Reverend Wheatcroft's reasoning behind not wanting his housekeeper to flick her duster around his study for fear of doing irreparable damage to his treasured possessions. His housekeeper was keen to inform the neighbourhood that her master was very particular about the contents of his study and that he wouldn't allow her to touch any of his precious books or papers! She knew to leave well alone, that books, papers and his study were his domain and his domain only.

Seeing the contents of his study in such disarray, let alone the dust that had accumulated, must have caused his housekeeper much consternation. She was, she said, unable to enter without him being present, for fear of also disrupting or accidentally rearranging, any of his books and papers. He had arranged these, according to him, in an orderly system, which in effect, appeared to be in no order at all.

The same disorder appeared to apply to the bureau, which had the flap down, revealing various manuscripts and letters piled haphazardly on its green leather worktop. The piles on either side of the desk allowed him just enough space in the middle to write all the correspondence that his job, as a busy town parish vicar, required him to do.

This was the first time I had seen inside Reverend Wheatcroft's impressive study. It was usually off limits to outsiders, so I had heard, for the reasons I've mentioned. So I felt privileged that he had allowed me inside to take a look. No wonder then, that his housekeeper rather anxiously led me to his study and reluctantly left me in there. She was no doubt miffed that Reverend Wheatcroft had allowed a mere youngster into his study with his valuable book collection. I continued standing politely, waiting for him to finish reading his newspaper.

I finally plucked up the courage to give a nervous cough to alert Reverend Wheatcroft to my presence, remembering that he was a little hard of hearing. He finally looked up, peering over the top of his newspaper at me. He extended to me a warm greeting and gave me an enquiring look, waiting I suspected, for me to prompt him and thus jog his memory as to why he had invited me to his study. I reminded him that he said he had a book in mind for me to borrow. With this prompt, he suddenly exclaimed that he had remembered and blamed his lack of memory on the many duties his job as vicar entailed. He then busied himself in search of the book, a task made more difficult by the scores of volumes that appeared randomly placed, in no particular chronological order.

He started rifling through the pile of papers covering the large, oval, mahogany reading table; it too, he had littered with his books and papers. I thought this was evidence of a cluttered mind but not so; it belied his logical mind, as his brain was usually as sharp as a razor. I don't know how he ever managed to find anything amongst the untidy pile!

On noticing that I had been observing the contents of his room, he asked me if I was admiring his book collection. He then informed me that he was a, "bibliophile", and observing that I, as a youngster, didn't understand, elaborated that he was "a collector and lover of books."

He told me that he had very old editions of the Bible, beautifully bound in embossed leather. Obviously, he used the Bible as the principle source for his sermons. He commented that the Bible was very educational and instructive and very pertinent to today. Its contents not only had historical significance, which was relevant to the era we were living in, but it spanned all of the humanities.

He then went on to give me a lecture on literature. He informed me that he proudly owned several first editions and rambled on about what titles he had. Forgetting at first, that being a mere youngster, I didn't fully understand what he was talking about. I didn't like to show my ignorance so I just listened in awe to what he had to say about his extensive book collection. I can recall a lot of what he told me, as his taste in reading fascinated me. It was my ambition to be well read like him.

He instructed me on the importance of first editions. These are often valued for being the first printed edition of a work, where the print run may have only produced several hundred copies, which were in circulation around the world. This is particularly so, if the book is the earlier work of an author before they had achieved fame and thus become more popular.

Reverend Wheatcroft stressed that it wasn't the monetary value of the book that interested him; it was the love of the book itself, to possess a thing of quality. Sometimes, with the added bonus of having beautiful illustrations, and or illustrative book dust covers ('dust jackets', as they are also called), drawn or painted by talented artists. He told me with pride that he had a first edition of Beatrix Potter's, 'Tales of Peter Rabbit', originally published in 1902, and exquisitely illustrated by the author herself. Unfortunately, he couldn't remember where he had stored it to show me.

He then alighted on a dusty old book, which he said he needed to handle with the utmost care, as it was an even older, antiquarian book. It too, was a first edition, published in 1859, entitled, '*On the Origin of Species by Means of Natural Selection* '; it was written by the famous naturalist, Charles Darwin. Reverend Wheatcroft told me that his father had handed down to him this important work by this author.

He went on to inform me that Darwin's book had preoccupied his father's generation; it became a topic for popular debate at the time of its publication, in the last century. He said his father was at that stage in his life, like I would be when I was a little older, when he began to question and seek answers to some of the big questions in life regarding man's existence and our place in the world. It was then that he began to search for alternative explanations to the meaning of life. Reverend Wheatcroft said '*On the Origin of Species*' had helped to shed some light on the topic and thereby raised some interesting arguments. He said he too, had also dipped into this book whilst still an undergraduate at Cambridge University.

Reverend Wheatcroft told me that he also collected contemporary and modern first editions. His preference was for those editions published in more recent times, for example, from the Forties to the present time, that is, the first half of the Fifties.

He mentioned that he had in his possession, the third volume in the trilogy, '*Roads to Freedom*' ('*Les Chemins de la Liberte*), entitled, '*Iron in the Soul*', translated from the French ('*La Mort dans Lam'e', 'Death in the Soul*'). Reverend Wheatcroft enthusiastically related to me an episode in the novel concerning the protagonist, an existentialist named, 'Mathieu: he heroically attempted to defend a French village during the war by shooting at their German attackers from the church bell-tower! (The English translation of this third volume in the trilogy, first published in 1950, was a year later than the French publication.)

The French writer Jean-Paul Sartre wrote the '*Roads to Freedom*' trilogy. He was also a well-known socialist and existentialist. Sartre became one of the leading exponents of existentialism in the twentieth century. This branch of philosophy came to prominence particularly after the Second World War.

Existentialism offered an alterative meaning to life in the midst of uncertainty, a mood created by the war and its aftermath.

The basic theory of Sartre's brand of existentialism, as I have come to understand it, is that the individual determines his or her own existence. The individual is a free agent responsible for their choices and actions, as oppose to being reliant on a supreme power, God. I became interested in existentialism when I was older and more able to understand it. I have since thought for a man of the cloth who believed in God to read about existentialism was rather a contradiction, but Reverend Wheatcroft was very worldly-wise and liked to keep an open mind and examine other viewpoints.

Reverend Wheatcroft also mentioned that he had a copy of William Cooper's, '*Scenes from Provincial Life*', which was published in 1950. He also said he had copies of the literary novels published in the early Fifties by the prominent literati at the time, Graham Greene.

Reverend Wheatcroft noted me glancing at a book lying on a small occasional table and told me it was a play entitled, '*The Browning Version*', by the playwright, Terence Rattigan. He then informed me that it was about an emotionally cold Classics master at a boys' public school who on retiring, reflects over his character flaws. Reverend Wheatcroft told me he had gone to see the play (published in 1949 in book form based on the 1948 play) staged in London. He said he had also seen the 1951 film, '*The Browning Version*'; it starred Michael Redgrave, Nigel Patrick and Jean Kent. Reverend Wheatcroft told me that it brought back memories of the public school he attended in his youth.

He also told me that he was looking forward to reading '*The Masters*' by C.P. Snow, about a fictional Cambridge University college and the internal politics involved in the selection of a new master. He said it had particularly appealed to him because he too, had been a student at Cambridge University. (I later learnt that this book published in 1951, was the fifth book in the series '*Strangers and Brothers*' by C.P. Snow. ('*The Masters*' was also the most popular and famous out of the series of eleven books, which spans several decades: written from 1940 to 1970.)

Reverend Wheatcroft informed me that he was currently rereading a novel by the famous writer George Orwell (the pseudonym for Eric Blair). The title was, '*Animal Farm: A Fairy*

Story'. He also informed me this book was first published just after the war in 1945. In the book, written in the form of an allegory with animals taking on human roles, the writer criticises totalitarianism.

Reverend Wheatcroft also had another novel by George Orwell, entitled *'Nineteen Eighty-Four'*. He informed me that this book was written in 1948 and published in 1949; the writer had, "transposed the year 1948 to 1984". In it the author imagines a future, nightmarish society ruled and watched over by 'Big Brother'. Reverend Wheatcroft called it a, "dystopian novel", (a vision of a nightmarish society, as oppose to a utopian one), which, in the view of the writer George Orwell, is a society ruled by totalitarianism. Reverend Wheatcroft said the book was, in essence, a criticism of totalitarianism in response to Stalin's dictatorship of Russia.

He said he also intended rereading, *'Nineteen Eighty-Four'*, in order to pay homage to a talented and perceptive writer, who had recently died, in January, 1950. As well as being a novelist, George Orwell was also an essayist, journalist, and critic. He died while only in his forties (at forty-six) from complications of tuberculosis (TB), which was rife in the Fifties, (as it had been in previous decades).

Reverend Wheatcroft went on to inform me that Britain had also lost another literary giant, whom he admired, George Bernard Shaw. He was awarded the Nobel Prize for Literature in 1925; he was a novelist, prolific playwright, critic and socialist activist. He died in his nineties (at ninety-four), in November of the same year, 1950, as George Orwell. Both writers were active socialists, which I think gave a hint of Reverend Wheatcroft's political affiliations. Being a maverick, it came as no surprise to me that he rebelled against his traditional conservative background.

He also delighted in telling me that he was "eclectic" in his "reading tastes". I observed several copies of the weekly magazine, *'Country Life'*, lying around Reverend Wheatcroft's study. I expect, for a bit of light reading, he enjoyed this magazine that covered rural pursuits, which, no doubt, satisfied his love of the countryside and his former home in the rural parts of the county of Cambridgeshire.

Reverend Wheatcroft was also a fan of science fiction. By the early Fifties this genre was at its height of popularity and receiving quite a following. '*The Martian Chronicles*' by American writer Ray Bradbury was published in 1950.

Ray Bradbury followed on from his success with his first hit, with his controversial dystopian novel, '*Fahrenheit 451*', published in 1953; this was also in the science fiction genre. This particular book was relevant to the period in the era of McCarthyism and the threat of book burning as a method of censorship, which is the premise of the book set in a futuristic world. (It is interesting to note that in subsequent publications, this book about censorship was ironically, itself subject to censorship!)

Reverend Wheatcroft had also read science fiction writer John Wyndham's apocalyptic novel 'The *Day of the Triffids*'. This was his most well-known and commercially successful science fiction novel, published in 1951.

Reverend Wheatcroft's favourite crime writer was Sir Arthur Conan Doyle, writing about his famous sleuth Sherlock Holmes; (these stories were first published between the end of the 1880's and the end of the 1920's). Reverend Wheatcroft mentioned that he had read, '*The Sherlock Holmes Long Stories, 4 Volumes in 1*' a reprint published in 1950.

I piped up by mentioning the ever popular Agatha Christie works of detective fiction; Reverend Wheatcroft quickly replied that her books were more to the taste of his housekeeper "Edie". "Especially, the aptly titled, '*Murder at the Vicarage*' " (first published in 1930), he said in a whisper, with a wicked grin spreading across his face. (Agatha Christie had several of her famous crime novels published throughout the first half of the Fifties.)

I heard once Reverend Wheatcroft got a television set, (before acquiring his own set he would watch it in someone else's home whenever the opportunity presented itself), he enjoyed watching the British Broadcasting Corporation (BBC) science fiction series, '*The Quatermass Experiment*'. The scriptwriter Nigel Kneale wrote this successful series. It was the first televised science fiction show and hugely popular, running to several series, with the first programme screened on 18th July, 1953.

The plot centred on a scientist, Professor Quatermass, who organises the first manned space rocket, which returns to earth with only one crew member who has undergone an alien metamorphosis;

he has turned into a plant-like creature that is capable of destroying all life on earth. Only Professor Quatermass can save the day! Reverend Wheatcroft used to enjoy telling his parishioners with a twinkle in his eye, that "Edie" his housekeeper "didn't approve" of him watching this series on television, as she found it "rather frightening!"

Since Reverend Wheatcroft was a fan of the writer George Orwell, I bet he also watched the BBC's '*Sunday Night Theatre*' live television adaptation of '*Nineteen Eighty-Four*'. It starred the actor Peter Cushing in the main role of Winston Smith. It had its television screening on 12th December, 1954.

I wondered if Reverend Wheatcroft had any meaningful discussions with my neighbours Miss Marsden who liked books, and also, our Mystery Man, an elderly, foreign neighbour who was fairly new to our neighbourhood. (I have also included in Volume III, along with Miss Marsden, a character study of our Mystery Man whom I also found intriguing.) They had to rely on the local public lending library to satisfy their reading appetites, since they were not in possession of their own personal library like Reverend Wheatcroft. This was especially true of our Mystery Man, who had to live as a lodger, within the confines of one small room in his landlady, Mrs Starling's house.

By the time Reverend Wheatcroft had finished discussing books, he appeared to have forgotten again why he had invited me. Then it seemed that what we had just been discussing earlier jogged his memory, as he cried out, "Ah, illustrations!" He resumed his search and finally found what he was looking for. He produced from the untidy heap, a book, which he was keen to inform me was penned at the beginning of this century, nearly fifty years ago, in 1908. He told me it was his favourite book as a child therefore he was keen to introduce it to other youngsters so that they could derive the same enjoyment from it, as he had. It was Kenneth Grahame's famous amphibian tale entitled, '*Wind in the Willows*'.

I was rather disappointed with Reverend Wheatcroft's choice of book, as I thought it rather childish for me. I had expected something more grown-up than '*Wind in the Willows*', but I didn't let my disappointment show. Apparently, this edition was a recently printed version, which appeared in 1950; it featured posthumously, the wonderful colour illustrations of Arthur Rackham, who was a famous children's illustrator. So at least it had plenty of colour illustrations in it, usually referred to as 'plates' back then. It also had plenty of food descriptions, which I obviously salivated over; we youngsters were prone to be obsessed with food, having to endure food rationing not only throughout the war and after but also throughout the first half of the Fifties!

While Reverend Wheatcroft had been searching for the book, I noticed displayed on the open, green baize top of the writing desk flap of the bureau, a partially written letter. Beside it was an ink well, and an impressive looking mottled brown tortoiseshell ink fountain pen. There were also sheaves of handsome letterheaded writing stationery lying nearby, with the vicarage address imprinted in the centre top edge of each sheet, just like on the unfinished letter.

The letterhead on the sheets of paper stated his job title, 'The Reverend', followed by his name, 'Ernest Wheatcroft' and his academic qualifications, 'MA (Cantab)'; this not only looked impressive to me but must have done so to the recipient. These were the same letters I had noticed after his name on our church noticeboard outside the church. I plucked up the courage to ask him what the letters stood for.

He informed me that he was a postgraduate of Cambridge University, having first attained the Bachelor Degree in Theology, which he helpfully informed me was the study of God. After graduating with a first degree, the University he attended automatically conferred on him a higher degree, (which is standard practice at Oxford, Cambridge and Dublin Universities), called a 'Master of Arts' degree, abbreviated to MA. He said this was in keeping with the historic tradition of the University going back hundreds of years. His master's degree was naturally in theology. He said at his University, (as in the two others mentioned), you only refer to the MA thereafter.

I asked him what 'Cantab' meant and he explained that 'Cantab' is the shortened version of the Latin word for Cambridge, which I have since looked up to refresh my memory. The Latin adjective Catabrigiensis (from the Latin noun Cantabrigia, meaning Cambridge), when paired with the Latin word (Universitas), means when translated, Cambridge University.

Reverend Wheatcroft explained that, "going up to Cambridge", was something of, "a family tradition", as both his father, and his father before him had also: "gone up to Cambridge, after attending a public school, as I had done." When he, "came down from Cambridge", he entered the priesthood and thus was also following in the, "family tradition", by following in the footsteps of both his father and grandfather who became men of the cloth. They became rectors serving in small countryside parishes.

I thought the fact that both his father and grandfather had been rectors had a rather quaint ring to it, reminding me, as it did, of the writers, Jane Austen and the three Bronte sisters, whose fathers were middle class country rectors. It seemed like Reverend Wheatcroft had had a rather idyllic, cosseted childhood, so was it any wonder that as a child he retained a belief in God. But I couldn't understand how he could retain this innocent belief in God when he was older, without being at all sceptical. Especially, having received the level of education he had, with its ultimate purpose, which was to teach one to question things, instead of just simply accepting things at face value.

Reverend Wheatcroft's religious beliefs puzzled me and he was, of course, perceptive enough to observe that I looked troubled. I explained that I couldn't understand why a highly educated man, such as him, could still believe in religion and the existence of God when there was no proof. I just couldn't fathom it out. He provided a rather plausible answer, which must have impressed me, as I can still remember it to this day.

"I suppose when one has been educated it propels one to search for the meaning of life, to question our existence; I, personally, have just been led in this direction, where religion satisfies some of the questions I've been asking." He added: "Maybe I have a greater propensity towards religion and the Church because of my calling, which is something that I've never really been able to fully explain."

He told me that when he was a young man he had a divine calling to offer his services to God. He elaborated by informing me, the calling to serve was partly inbred in him following on from his forefathers who were all drawn to serve in the house of God. He stated once more that it had been something of a family tradition with his father, and his grandfather, entering the Church as a profession, so naturally he was drawn to the Church from an early age.

He tried to explain to me what life would be like without religion in his life, using an analogy, which he appeared quite chuffed with, as it made him chuckle: "Without religion in my life would be like not wearing that cassock I've become so accustomed to wearing; I wouldn't feel properly clothed without it!" I could understand his sentiment, since religion and the Church had always been a part of his life; this is the only life he knew. Religion and the Church, no doubt, provided a comfort for him; it was the backbone of his daily life. He told me, he would feel "bereft without it."

* * *

I had some interesting little discussions with Reverend Wheatcroft during the time that he served within our parish. He tried to explain his faith to me in the hope I think, of instilling me with faith, which for all his efforts didn't work! I was, and still am an atheist. I went to church as a matter of habit because it was customary to do so; I could never bring myself to believe in the Almighty. I questioned the existence of God and couldn't come up with any satisfactory answers that satisfied my enquiring mind. I personally couldn't understand Reverend Wheatcroft's faith; my lack of faith arose from when I first started to attend church.

Reverend Wheatcroft wasn't offended; he took my disbelief in good faith. He put it down to my questioning mind and said I would eventually turn to God later in life, but it was important that I first had to find my way in the world and seek answers to all the questions I had. He thought it was healthy to question, to possess an enquiring mind and think for oneself, that we shouldn't all follow like sheep. So in this way he was also unconventional, in that he didn't believe everyone should conform and tow the line.

He said it was only natural for an intelligent person to question, and explained that he too, went through all these questions and doubts in the beginning of his religious education, just as his father had done before him. He said like him, I too, was a thinker. This pleased me no end, much to my neighbour and grammar school pupil Jeremy's irritation, when I told him. He thought being a thinker was exclusive to him, since he was the only one in our street to have passed the eleven-plus examination; this allowed him access to a grammar school education, where thinking was, and is, actively encouraged.

I think Reverend Wheatcroft saw in me a kindred soul, at least that's what I used to like to imagine. I so wanted him to think highly of me and believe I was capable of great things when I was older. I don't think he secretly held out much hope for some of the others, though.

I think I speak not only for myself but for the majority of his parishioners, when I say Reverend Wheatcroft was highly revered in our neighbourhood. I greatly admired him for his intellect, wit, good humour, kindness and enthusiasm for all he undertook in life.

Reverend Wheatcroft continued serving our parish until his retirement in the mid-Fifties. Church attendances were noticeably dwindling considerably by then, so it was just as well. It meant that he did not have to experience an almost empty church; this would have been very disheartening for a gregarious personality such as his. During the time he served as our vicar he could always count on our church being filled to capacity with a full congregation, since he was such an extremely popular figure in our community.

Unfortunately, Reverend Wheatcroft's retirement meant that he had to leave the large vicarage he had made his home to make way for his new incumbent. I, like many in the neighbourhood, was very sad to see him go. He was probably the most popular vicar we've ever had serving our community; he certainly had a strong following in our neighbourhood.

I heard he returned to his home town of Cambridgeshire and took up residence in a small cottage in a countryside village on the outskirts. I also heard on the grapevine that Reverend Wheatcroft's devoted housekeeper Miss Herbert moved to be near him so that she could stay on and look after him. As I mentioned before, she had no other family, so it made perfect sense to carry on with her domestic duties for her employer rather than submit to a life of loneliness.

After all, Reverend Wheatcroft was not a man who was used to looking after himself. He had always been able to rely on someone to take care of the daily, domestic chores, including cooking his meals; these domestic services were provided for him at the boarding school and at the university that he attended in his youth.

In his working life as a vicar he was fortunate enough to be able to afford the services of a housekeeper. So it was totally understandable that he had come to rely on his trusted housekeeper whom he was also fond of. They had a mutual respect for each other.

But Reverend Wheatcroft still continued to take an active part, albeit a back seat, in both our church and in the community at large, when he was in our neighbourhood. Of course, as a friend and past servant of our church he always received invitations to the big functions. Any time when there was a splendid spread you could always count on Reverend Wheatcroft to be there in attendance! I look back on his time serving our neighbourhood and parish with very fond memories.

A Retired Couple, Mr and Mrs Green Who Lived Opposite

Mr and Mrs Green lived virtually opposite our house, in a bungalow. They were a childless couple, probably in their sixties. Since Mr Green had retired from his job in what was the burgeoning manufacturing industry in the Fifties, I was able to observe their daily activities throughout the day, that is, when I was not at school of course. Mrs Green because she was married never worked, as far as I was aware.

Married women tended to be stay-at-home housewives back in the Fifties; however, they worked during the war helping with the war effort, while the men were away fighting. Mrs Green probably worked in a munitions factory then, lots of women without children to look after did this kind of work, although Mrs Green could have been too old. Mr Green was probably in the Home Guard, (a local defence volunteer), since he was too old for active service. However, that was in the past, now they were both mainly at home.

I knew their daily routine, which was boringly predictable, but I still enjoyed observing their particular idiosyncrasies all the same. Like their surname Green, which is a very common name, such as Brown, Jones and Smith, they too, were nothing out of the ordinary.

Mrs Green was a notorious gossip, while her husband was the quiet, unassuming one who preferred to stay in the background. She may only have been small in statue compared to her husband who was taller, but she was the domineering one of the two. She gave all the orders and he undertook all the hard work. He was as thin as a bean pole, which wasn't surprising with all the chores he had to undertake.

I would often hear Mrs Green calling out to her husband, "Derek, where are you!" Then giving instructions to her husband, "Derek, I want this done." "Derek, stop what you're doing now and come and do this!" She would point at what she wanted doing next. When she was admonishing him she would exclaim in her shrill voice, "No Derek, no!" Or, "Leave that alone!"

Mr Green usually placated his wife by agreeing to her demands; I would overhear him reply, "Yes dear", and "Coming dear", when his wife nagged at him, which was often! He appeared to be a little afraid of her. I think he had probably grown tired of arguing back and so had learnt to say little and ignore her constant complaints, rather than exacerbate the situation: he preferred a quiet life.

I never did find out her Christian name, it was probably a closely guarded secret. She preferred people to refer to her as Mrs Green; to her it probably conferred status. She didn't want to be referred to as a spinster, like one of our neighbours, Miss Marsden, who lived with her elderly, frail mother. (I have included a character study of her in Volume III.) If that's all Mrs Green could aspire to, to be married, I pity her!

I rarely saw Mrs Green smile; she reserved that for special occasions that merited it. Such as when she was in conversation with the vicar, Reverend Wheatcroft and putting on airs and graces, or in the company of the ladies at the Women's Institute (WI), when it suited her.

Her plump, round face that wrinkled when she screwed up her face in a scowl, which was often, reminded me of a pumpkin. Her small, round, wire-rimmed spectacles, which she wore firmly, fixed on the end of her small, pug shaped nose, made her harsh countenance more pronounced.

Her husband, unlike her, had a cheerful countenance and was friendlier. Mr Green always courteously raised his trilby, not minding in the least, if he was exposing his balding head to the harsh, cold winds that were prevalent during the Fifties. He always had a smile and a wave at the ready when he saw us children, while his wife looked on with that almost permanent scowl on her sullen face. She could be intimidating with her stare. I think Mr Green liked children, whereas, Mrs Green didn't: perhaps that's why they didn't have any children of their own.

They were as different as chalk and cheese. I don't know what they had in common really. From what I had sampled of Mrs Green's baking when Mr Green kindly offered it to us children when her back was turned, she was a good cook; they say the way to a man's heart is through his stomach. Or maybe she was gentler in her youth and the passing years had soured her. Perhaps when she was young she caught his eye with her youthful beauty, which had now faded with age. Maybe they had tired of each other's personal habits. Now they just tolerated each other.

Mr Green liked to indulge, when he could, in various outdoor pursuits and hobbies that allowed him an opportunity to escape from his wife. But this wasn't often. The daily chores of maintaining a property and garden took up most of the day, before the advent of labour-saving devices, which came on the market and were more affordable towards the latter part of the decade. Mr Green would help his wife with the cleaning chores that needed doing.

Any spare time he had he would attend the cinema, at least once a week. It offered him a welcome escape from being henpecked by his spouse. The cinema offered the British population, as a whole, a welcome escapism from the austere times they were living in, in the post-war first half of the fifties. Cinemas' transported their audiences into a world of glamour and fantasy, as they watched, in the plush interiors of the cinema, their film idols living the kind of life they could only dream about.

Mr Green's trips to the cinema also enabled him to have a dose of realism, if one was wanted, with the up-to-date documentary accounts provided by '*Pathe-News*' on what was happening in the world beyond his doorstep. He could also enjoy, apart from the main feature, a 'B-movie' (the subsidiary, low-budget film), and trailers for forthcoming films, including advertisements; cinema-goers like Mr Green certainly got their money's worth.

I had heard he used to enjoy going to the cinema several times a week, particularly in the Forties, in common with most of the population it seems; cinema audiences reached there peak in 1946. However, Mrs Green had attempted to curb his visits by getting him to spend more time at home on the domestic front. Occasionally, they went to the cinema together as a couple, but not, I suspected, as much as they used to do in their courting days and in the early days of their marriage.

Since Mrs Green was a Humphrey Bogart fan, she attended with her husband, so I heard on the grapevine, the screening of the Hollywood adventure film, '*The African Queen*', after it was released in 1951, which also starred the legendary Katherine Hepburn.

Mr Green was no match for the rugged Mr Bogart. Mr Bogart's tough-guy image appealed to Mrs Green; he was everything that her husband wasn't. He played mysterious, brooding characters, answerable to no one. He indulged in the vices of womanising, drinking, smoking and gambling, in his tough-guy film portrayals. Vices that Mrs Green did not allow Mr Green to indulge in, certainly not in her company! Mr Bogart was someone who could put Mrs Green in her place, just with one menacing look!

Mrs Green made it known that she was a fan of the old movie stars of the silver screen, like Humphrey Bogart. She probably went to see the 1950, Hollywood film drama, 'Sunset Boulevard'. It starred Gloria Swanson, as a fading movie star of the silent screen; her co-star was William Holden, who made a foothold in the film industry with his Oscar nominated role.

Mrs Green was a huge fan of the great American actress, Bette Davis. I expect she associated herself with the strong, assertive female characters Bette Davis was renowned for playing. I also heard on the grapevine that Mrs Green got her husband to go with her to see Bette Davis in the Hollywood film released for public viewing in 1950, entitled, 'All About Eve', which won an American Academy award for 'Best Picture'.

'All About Eve' centred on the relationship between Ms. Davis' character, as aging actress, 'Margo Channing', and a young fan, played by Joan Fontaine, who ingratiates herself into Ms. Channing's life, and then attempts to undermine her both in her professional and personal life. I suspected that the irony was lost on Mrs Green; she was more like the fan in this instance: she was constantly trying to undermine her husband but more overtly.

Mrs Green was also a fan of thrillers and of the well-known British-born director of thrillers, Alfred Hitchcock. She must have seen the 1950 Hitchcock thriller, 'Stage Fright', starring Jane Wyman, Marlene Dietrich, Michael Wilding and Richard Todd. And 'Strangers on a Train', released in 1951, starring Farley Granger, Robert Walker and Ruth Roman. Also, 'Rear Window', starring James Stewart and Grace Kelly, and 'Dial M for Murder'; again starring Grace Kelly and co-starring Ray Milland. Both these films went on general release in 1954.

Mr Green was a fan of war films, of which there were many, not only during the war but also after in the post-war era. World War Two, of course, was still fresh in people's memories. Watching films, particularly war films during the war helped to instil patriotism and raise morale on the home front. The government used war films as an effective propaganda tool to win support for the Allied cause.

The 1950 Hollywood drama, 'The Men' starred Marlon Brando in his film debut, as an injured American veteran of World War Two; he has to deal with the mental scars caused by his physical injuries sustained during that war which has left him as a paraplegic. This award-winning film centres on his fraught relationship with his fiancée played by Teresa Wright.

The Hollywood film, The Caine Mutiny', released in 1954, was about a United States World War Two Naval Destroyer and Minesweeper, and the court martial of two of its serving officers. Since it starred Humphrey Bogart, Mrs Green might have accompanied Mr Green on that occasion. There was also the Hollywood film, 'Stalag 17', shown in 1953, set in a German prisoner of war camp, starring William Holden, who for his role, won an Academy Award for Best Actor.

Apparently, Mr Green wanted to go and see the American World War Two film, 'From Here to Eternity', which was showing in the cinemas in 1953, and which also won Academy awards, including for 'Best Picture'. It was a drama about the social and professional lives of three American soldiers stationed at the naval base in Pearl Harbour, Hawaii, prior to the attack on Pearl Harbour. There was a rumour circulating in the neighbourhood that Mrs Green was having none of it; she wouldn't allow Mr Green to go, saying the film was too salacious! Although, I don't think she used the word 'salacious', as that word, I'm sure, was not in her vocabulary! According to all the publicity surrounding the film, she must have also been referring to its steamy beach scene, starring Burt Lancaster and the very attractive British actress, Deborah Kerr, in a rather revealing, tight-fitting bathing costume.

Mr Green had better luck going to see, on his own, another war film of the same year, 1953, 'The Cruel Sea'. A British film about the battle of the Atlantic between the British Royal Navy and the German Navy, starring Jack Hawkins, Donald Sinden and Virginia McKenna. I heard him discussing it enthusiastically with a neighbour. Mr Green had himself served in the Royal Navy during World War One and was very proud of the fact.

He probably also saw the 1954, World War Two British film, '*The Sea Shall Not Have Them*', about a British aircraft crew stranded in the North Sea after a forced landing. It starred Dirk Bogarde, Michael Redgrave and Anthony Steel. There was also the Second World War British drama based on the true story of three POW escapees from a German prisoner of war camp, '*The Wooden Horse*', starring Leo Genn, David Tomlinson and Anthony Steel. It was one of the most popular films in 1950 when it went on general release. Another popular World War Two film based on a true story, which Mr Green must have gone to see was, '*The Dam Busters*', (released in 1955, it was the most popular film in Britain that year). The film is about how the British managed to attack German dams with a newly invented bouncing bomb, thus flooding Germany's industrial base and hindering their war effort. It starred Richard Todd as RAF Wing Commander Guy Gibson; the pilots carry out the successful mission under his command. Michael Redgrave played Dr. Barnes Wallis the bomb's inventor.

Another British war drama popular with British cinemagoers, was a film entitled '*Odette*', it was released in 1950. It was a biopic of an extremely brave female, French-born British secret agent assisting the French resistance. (Odette Sansom became the first woman to receive the George Cross for her bravery during the Second World War.) The film starred Anna Neagle and Trevor Howard as the main leads.

'*Angels One Five*', was yet another popular box office British war drama, it was released for public viewing in 1952. The plot centres on an RAF fighter pilot and his squadron during the Battle of Britain. It starred Jack Hawkins, John Gregson, and real life husband and wife, Michael Denison and Dulcie Gray.

Another popular British film was, '*The Malta Story*', released in 1953, about the British RAF's defence of Malta against attack and invasion during World War Two, a strategically important island for the Allies. It starred Alec Guinness, Jack Hawkins, Anthony Steel and Muriel Pavlow. Mrs Green didn't object to British stiff upper lip, gritty World War Two dramas.

I used to spot Mr Green exiting our local cinemas; we had several cinemas including, the Gaumont, Odeon, Rivoli and the Ritz. There were also other cinemas in neighbouring towns. I would glance up at the billboard to see what he had been watching.

It appeared that he saw all the latest releases. These included the Hollywood film noirs: 'The Asphalt Jungle', released in 1950, and the thriller 'Niagara', made in Technicolor and released in 1953. I suspect that Mr Green's spouse would not have approved of him seeing these crime dramas, which also notably starred Marilyn Monroe, the sex goddess of the silver screen. She achieved, for the first time, top billing in the screen credits of the latter film, playing a femme fatale who schemes to murder her husband, played by Joseph Cotton.

Ms. Monroe's following films in the first half of the decade cemented her status as a sex symbol; this probably prompted Mrs Green to also object to her husband going to see these popular vehicles revealing Ms. Monroe's many talents. Ms. Monroe displayed her comic abilities in the musical comedies, 'How to Marry a Millionaire', and 'Gentlemen Prefer Blondes'. In the former film Ms. Monroe's co-stars were the leggy Betty Grable and the beguiling beauty, Lauren Becall. While her co-star in the latter film was that other voluptuous sex symbol, brunette bombshell Jane Russell. Both Hollywood films went on release for public viewing in 1953. In 1954, Ms. Monroe starred in the musical 'There's No Business Like Show Business'.

I expect Mr Green consoled himself by going to watch American westerns, such as the multi-academy award-winning, 'High Noon', released in 1952. Its principal stars were, Gary Cooper, Grace Kelly, Lloyd Bridges, Lee Van Cleef and Katy Jurado. It is widely viewed as the best western ever made.

However, some regard the western, 'Shane', produced and directed by George Steven, and starring Alan Ladd, Jack Palance, Van Heflin, Jean Arthur, and Brandon de Wilde, to be the best western ever made. And certainly the best of the westerns made in the Fifties. It was made in full Technicolor, (winning an Oscar for photography), and used the new flat, widescreen. It went on general release in 1953.

Other westerns produced in this era, as the titles suggest, included: 'Broken Arrow', released in 1950, starring James Stewart, Jeff Chandler and rising star, the beautiful Debra Paget. There was also 'Arrowhead', in 1953, starring Charlton Heston and Jack Palance. And 'Broken Lance', in 1954, which starred Spencer Tracey, Richard Widmark, Richard Wagner and Jean Peters. The last two films also starred the Mexican, exotic looking beauty, and award-winning actress Katy Jurado.

The Hollywood film industry were doing all they could in the Fifties to produce bigger and better films in an attempt to entice audiences, which had been steadily declining since the late Forties, back to the cinema. (Cinema audiences in Britain peaked in 1946, a point I made earlier.) The industry's response to the lure of television that was drawing audiences away from the cinema was to invest in new technology, with wider screens, improved sound and picture quality. They even used special effect 3-D images. They also invested in extravagant, mammoth productions with huge, costly sets and lavish costumes. The industry also employed a staggeringly large cast of extras for each production. Hence the biblical epic was born.

Britain was a religious nation in the Fifties so Mr Green had a plausible excuse to go and watch these biblical epics. The first of these Hollywood blockbusters was the 1949 film, 'Samson and Delilah', shown in cinemas in 1950, starring Victor Mature and the Hollywood beauty Hedy Lamarr. It was apparently the most popular film in Britain for that year, not surprising, considering it was the cinema's first biblical epic.

'Quo Vadis', in 1951, was another mammoth biblical production with a huge cast, notably starring, Robert Taylor, Deborah Kerr, Leo Genn and Peter Ustinov. It was reputed to be the highest grossing film for the Hollywood production company MGM, second only to, 'Gone with the Wind', (released in 1939). Also released for public viewing in 1951, was 'David and Bathsheba'; it starred Gregory Peck and Susan Hayward.

The 1953 biblical epic, 'The Robe', was also one of the first films shown in the new CinemaScope, which featured an innovative widescreen. It starred Richard Burton in his second notable screen role (his first was in, 'My Cousin Rachel', in 1952), alongside Jean Simmons. The sequel to 'The Robe' released the following year was, 'Demetrius and the Gladiators', starring Victor Mature and Susan Hayward. The 1954 biblical film, 'The Silver Chalice', went on release for public viewing in Britain, in 1955. Notably, it starred Paul Newman in his film debut; it also starred, Virginia Mayo, Pier Angeli and Jack Palance.

*   *   *

When Mr Green wasn't attending the cinema, another of his favourite outdoor pursuits was coarse fishing, which was a very popular hobby in the Fifties. In fact, angling was, and still is, the most popular participant sport in Britain since the Second World War. Greyhound racing though was extremely popular back then, in fact, the most popular spectator sport after football.

Greyhound racing started to become popular in the Thirties, in large part due to betting on course, which was the only form of betting that was legal. But I don't think Mrs Green would allow her spouse to go to the dogs, especially not to place bets, or, 'have a flutter', as it was often called.

As for pigeon racing, which was also popular, it was just beyond the pale, just too working class for Mrs Green. Besides, she didn't want Mr Green messing about wasting his time with carrier pigeons sending messages, as they were used during the war. Although, I bet she wasn't averse to eating pigeon pie: this is what people ate during wartime when they kept other domestic fowls mainly for their egg production.

Mr Green was probably such a keen fisherman because it gave him an opportunity to escape from his wife's clutches for much of the day. When he went fishing though, it often meant that he would have to rise early in the morning, at such an ungodly hour, as four or five am!

If I happened to awaken very early in the morning around that time, I would peer out of my bedroom window and I would occasionally see Mr Green setting off at the crack of dawn with his long fishing rods and fishing paraphernalia. He probably closed his front door behind him as quietly as he could and crept down the path and opened and closed the wooden gate with care so as not to disturb Mrs Green, who I suspect was still sleeping. He was absent *with* leave, as his wife had obviously given her consent. He was gone all day and didn't return until just before dusk.

I don't know what Mr Green did with all that time on his hands, sitting on a river bank or the edge of a canal, staring at his float in the water, waiting for hours on end for the fish to bite. He probably had a much needed man to man chat with the other angling enthusiasts, a place where he was free to talk about his spouse behind her back without fear of any comeback.

I was surprised that Mrs Green allowed her husband this indulgence to go fishing. Perhaps it allowed her to indulge in her hobby of gossiping with the neighbours since he wasn't around for her to boss him about. Perhaps she was rewarding him with time off for good behaviour. He would then have been more willing to oblige her, not so begrudgingly, when she had further chores lined up for him to do. She certainly seemed to have him well trained.

Mr Green, in common with a lot of coarse fishing enthusiasts, sometimes enjoyed simply catching fish, such as roach, bream and carp, just for the pleasure of checking its weight. Anglers liked indulging in 'Match Fishing' competitions, with bets waged, in spite of unregulated betting being illegal back then, (a point I mentioned earlier). (This was, of course, before the Betting and Gaming Act, introduced in 1960, which took effect from 1961, legalised off course betting.) Anglers would bet amongst themselves on who had caught the heaviest amount of a particular species of fish, or the greatest variety of fish, before carefully throwing the fish back in the water.

To get his wife on side, Mr Green would make sure that every so often he wouldn't return home empty-handed. He would try and bring back the day's catch for their supper. Perhaps herring or even mackerel, depending on the season, of course, and where he was fishing but more often than not, eels caught from local rivers and reservoirs.

I'm surprised Mrs Green didn't object to having to gut fish in her kitchen and having to smell the foul fishy odour, which lingered for days afterwards. Probably in those lean times when rationing was still in place, she was thankful that they had something to supplement their meagre diet. It would also mean that they could spend what few points they had left in their ration booklets for other foods that were on the points system.

Although fish was never on ration, not even during wartime, it was still in short supply; there were always long queues at the fishmongers. (Although it helped living in a coastal town where there was some local fish to purchase). During the war, fishermen were not able to fish in the mine-infested waters of the Atlantic, and able-bodied seaman and their fishing vessels were commandeered for the war effort. What is more, there was no price control over the price of fish caught, so it could be expensive for the average consumer.

Mrs Green used to pass on the fish remains of her husband's local catch back to him; he would then pass them on, under his wife's orders, to Mrs Trenchard, another of our gossipy neighbours (also featured in this Volume). She would then give these fishy titbits to her precious cat, Humphrey, who was, no doubt, very grateful.

While Mr Green fished, Mrs Green baked. Mrs Green set aside a day every week for baking: Fridays. Most housewives kept to a strict routine for doing their household chores. Usually, Fridays were set aside for baking for the weekend and for the following week.

No wonder then that Mrs Green either banished Mr Green to the garden and his potting shed, or agreed to him going fishing, or to the cinema. She didn't want him getting under her feet when she was busy with baking. As with most things, baking requires time and effort, which is probably why she liked to have an empty kitchen and bungalow so she wouldn't be disturbed. Her husband was quite willing to oblige, as he was only too grateful to be given the time off to escape her constant bickering and pursue his own interests for a change.

I could often smell the delicious baking aromas wafting outside from Mrs Green's back kitchen on a Friday. She baked all manner of delicious fare: cakes, pies, puddings, tarts, scones, bread and buns.

Mrs Green, in common with many housewives, had to learn to be resourceful with what limited ingredients she had to work with because of the many years of rationing; in fact, the British population had to endure fourteen years of rationing, both during and after the war. Mrs Green was therefore very capable of stretching what provisions they had, to provide both her and her husband with enough satisfying meals for the week.

People often had to use their ingenuity when creating meals using mock ingredients in place of rationed or difficult to obtain ingredients. Mock cream (made from cornflour, milk, margarine, sugar and a few drops of vanilla essence), and artificial sweeteners, were two such items.

With sugar rationed, carrots, parsnips, turnips, sweet potato and beetroot, were used as a substitute sweetener in puddings and cakes, just as these had been used during the war. If people couldn't get hold of eggs, they would used powdered dried (dehydrated) eggs instead of the real thing, and the same for milk, they would use a powdered substitute.

During the war, the Ministry of Food provided useful recipes using the memorable cartoon character, 'Doctor Carrot', along with another cartoon character, 'Potato Pete', on the covers of recipe booklets. 'Doctor Carrot' publicized the nutritious benefits of vitamin A. Mrs Green was therefore well versed in the art of providing nutritious meals for herself and Mr Green.

Mrs Green really went to town with her baking when fats came off ration in May, 1954. Some of her baking efforts she donated to the church for their fetes, fairs and the harvest festival, and for the Women's Institute (WI) meetings, and of course, for the vicar, Reverend Wheatcroft. He never went without!

The only time I got to sample her fare, (apart from when her husband gave us children some leftovers), was at the WI run, church cake stall, where I or my mother had to pay a ha'penny or two for the privilege. Mrs Green was immensely proud of her baking. She competed with the other women of the WI and aimed to bake the most risen and the softest sponge, as she didn't like to be outdone in anything!

On one occasion, I remember when Mr Green kindly offered us children some fairy cakes, when Mrs Green was, of course, out at her weekly trip to the hairdresser's. He called us children over when we were playing in the street and allowed us to help ourselves to the little sponge cakes, offered to us on a large plate, which he said, were becoming a little stale. I don't think Mr Green had much of a sweet tooth so he wanted to dispense with the iced fairy cakes before his wife returned home.

Mr and Mrs Green learnt not to waste anything, which was something they learnt with food rationing, along with the rest of the population, most notably during the war. 'Waste Not Want Not', was a Second World War motto, in times of rations and shortages. Mr Green certainly didn't want the cakes to go to waste and thought we would appreciate them. He was right: they were delicious made with all that sweet icing sugar, once sugar was off ration. He knew we wouldn't let on to Mrs Green; it was our little secret. She would simply assume that he had consumed the cakes.

I had to admit, rather reluctantly, that Mrs Green was awfully good at baking. It's probably a skill passed down from her mother, and her mother before her. I'm glad because it meant that her spouse Mr Green was usually well fed; he needed to be in order to carry out all the chores and running around he had to do for her, which also probably explained why he remained as thin as a beanpole.

Mr Green's other interest was his garden, and in particular, his small allotment at the back of the garden. During the war when food shortages were at their height, the government encouraged the population to 'Dig for Victory' and 'Grow Your Own Vegetables'. Those without a garden were encouraged to own an allotment on a designated public plot of land, which proved very popular. Every available space was utilised for this purpose, including the national parks in London; there were even allotments in the moat surrounding the Tower of London!

Mr Green kept a few chickens in his back garden, in common with a lot of neighbours. People often kept chickens, along with pigs and rabbits; it was a habit left over from the war years of rationing when people were encouraged to rear their own livestock and grow their own vegetables, due to the food shortages.

However, after the devastating, highly infectious viral disease, myxomatosis, which affects rabbits, virtually wiped out the rabbit population in Britain in 1953, people were no longer able to keep rabbits. The virus had been introduced into Australia in 1950, and later in France in 1952, to control the rabbit population, as these animals were viewed as agricultural pests that ruined crops. Thereafter, the virus spread across Europe, arriving in Britain around September with the first confirmed case in the South-East county of Kent, in October, 1953.

Mr Green also prized his potting shed, where he could escape from his spouse and spend as many hours as he was allowed to by her. He also had a couple of bee hives in his back garden, which came in useful, as he used the honey as a sugar substitute when sugar was on ration. Beekeeping was a useful resource, which he had learnt to make use of during the war when encouraged to do so in the 'Dig for Victory' campaign. The government continued its propaganda after the war with, 'Dig for Victory and After'. This encouraged the population to continue with self-sufficiency in order to supplement their meagre post-war diets when food rationing and shortages were still in force.

Mr Green said the proceeds from his garden allotment and potting shed provided produce for his wife to do her cooking and baking, and hence, provided much needed food for the table. Mrs Green, for her part, had learnt to make good use of her husband's fruit and vegetable crops. Of course, like most people, what they ate was dictated by what was in season. Mrs Green was always in need of a constant supply of root vegetables in the long winters for her warming stews, and seasonal fruit for her delicious fruit pies, tarts and puddings.

Mr Green must have been green fingered, as most years he was lucky enough to be rewarded with an abundant crop of fruit and vegetables. According to him, "the more you pick the more you'll get". He always grew runner beans, and more often than not, had a bumper crop. I used to see them in summer time, strung up on long, thin bean poles, criss-crossed in the shape of a wigwam and tied together near the top. I also remember he had raspberry canes.

Mr Green also harvested in the summer: tomatoes, lettuces, cucumbers, shallots, onions, spring onions, radishes, gooseberries, strawberries and redcurrants. He also harvested one of my favourite fruits, rhubarb; its delicious sweet stalks used in desserts are actually classed as a vegetable!

Mr and Mrs Green also had an apple tree and a pear tree in their garden. His other winter crop would also consist of savoy cabbages, carrots, cauliflowers, swedes, turnips, parsnips, kale, broccoli, sprouts, spinach, marrows, leeks, peas and broad beans, beetroot, and of course, potatoes.

Potato, was, and is, a staple food, and was the main ingredient of the famous, (Lord) Woolton Pie. This nourishing dish was served and eaten everywhere: in domestic kitchens, hotels, restaurants and food canteens. (It was created for the Ministry of Food by the head chef Francois Latry at the Savoy Hotel in London, and named after Lord Woolton, the then Minister of Food.) The pie posed as a steak and kidney pie but was missing those two main ingredients when meat was in such short supply. The pie contained potatoes, cauliflower, carrots, swede and a few spring onions, (or any seasonal vegetables) in an oatmeal stock, topped with a pastry crust and served with plain brown gravy; it was, in effect, a vegetable pie. I don't think anyone was fooled by the disguise!

The only time when the government rationed potatoes was during the 'Big Freeze', in the first quarter of 1947. It was the harshest winter the population had ever known in living memory. I don't know how Mr Green coped with his garden and allotment, along with the rest of the population. That devastating winter destroyed crops, which remained frozen in the ground. To break up the frozen soil, people had to use pneumatic drills! The long winter with heavy snow drifts and freezing temperatures, dragged on from January through to March, resulting in major flooding after all the snow had melted, which once again was responsible for damaging crops.

Growing such a variety of fruit and vegetables ensured that Mr Green always had a good supply if several failed to produce a good crop. Most of the produce was preserved for the rest of the year in plain glass jam jars and the larger glass Kilner jars, which have special screw top metal lids to create an airtight seal. Preserving fruit and vegetables was naturally encouraged during the war.

The ladies of the Women's Institute, used to preserve a lot of fruit for their famed jam-making by canning it with the aid of canning machinery. This specialised machinery was on loan during the war from the United States of America. They also kindly supplied other useful paraphernalia for producing the finished product of jars of jam. The land girls who belonged to the Women's Land Army (WLA) during the war also used to preserve the fruit from the land by this method.

Mr Green donated quite a bit of their produce to the church harvest festival in October, and of course, to the church fetes and fairs in the spring and summer, and at Christmas. Mr Green also sometimes kindly gave our mothers some of his crop, without his wife's knowledge, of course.

Mr Green liked to listen to the popular, professional gardener, Percy Thrower, on the radio for gardening tips. Mr Thrower takes credit for being the first well-known gardening personality. However, Mr Green wouldn't have been able to listen to the popular 'Gardeners' Question Time', the world's longest running Gardeners' radio programme, as it was only heard in the Northern region until it went nationwide in 1957. (It started in 1947, under its original title 'How Does Your Garden Grow'.

Mr Green was such an enthusiastic gardener and grower that he tried to get us youngsters interested. He once managed to invite a few of us youngsters into his back garden when his wife wasn't about. I remember him carefully explaining to us how to cultivate a peach. I don't know how he managed to obtain one, perhaps he had grown it. He told us that we should keep the stone that he kindly gave us and plant it in the garden, preferably on a south facing wall to catch the sun, and water it and watch it grow.

We waited and waited patiently for weeks, but nothing happened, nothing grew from the soil. Then Mr Green explained that for the fruit tree to reach maturity and start bearing fruit, if we were lucky and it germinated, the process could take several years! We became bored at that point: it put us off growing anything if we had to wait that long to see the fruits of our labours, excuse the pun. According to Mr Green, to "reap what you sow" required patience, which was something we youngsters didn't have! As youngsters, we wanted and expected immediate success.

Mr Green used to enter his vegetables in the local horticultural show. I recall when the large marrow he had entered was awarded runner-up. He was very proud of that moment, and had a bigger grin on his face than usual for weeks after. He tried to explain to us that a small marrow was a courgette and showed us the difference in size. We couldn't understand how he could get so excited about the size and weight of his marrows, like the fish he caught; it would have been different if it was cake!

It was the same with Mrs Green's, prize-winning roses: she was extremely proud of her rose growing accomplishments. Roses were one of the most popular flowers in the Fifties, if not the most popular.

She would enter her favourite rose, the 'Peace' rose in the local horticultural shows. A creamy yellowy rose, tinged with pink, which was a variety that was also a universal favourite in post-war Britain; so named as a poignant celebration of what our nation had gone through to achieve peace.

Mr and Mrs Green seemed to compete against each other at the local horticultural shows and fairs. Mrs Green, in an attempt at one-upmanship, would boast that she had been awarded more coloured rosettes and certificates for her roses, than her husband for his fruit and vegetable produce. And in an attempt to outdo her husband, she would goad him in public about her superiority in attaining the

Royal Horticultural Show's, 'Award of Garden Merit'. She would often emasculate her husband like this in public! She would argue that her 'First Class Certificate', was far higher in the pecking order than a mere, 'Preliminary Commendation', which her husband had won.

Like her award-winning 'Peace' rose, peace reined supreme in Mr and Mrs Green's household because Mr Green wisely undertook domestic duties when instructed by Mrs Green. When it came to their front garden, which housed her much prized roses, Mrs Green again won hands down, as she dished out the orders. Mr Green mowed the lawn every weekend in spring and summer, while Mrs Green tended her beloved but thorny roses, which lined the borders of their front garden path.

She was prickly like her roses, as she would easily take offence if anyone dared to find fault with her precious roses, or anything else for that matter! She also left all the weeding and tidying of the borders, including trimming the privet hedge, which formed a boundary between many gardens back in those days, to Mr Green. She busied herself with carefully pruning her roses.

I enjoyed watching them as they undertook these chores in view of the neighbours, when they were not masked by the hedges and greenery in their garden. She would get Mr Green to dig out plants or old stock and re-site them, or plant her newly acquired shrubs. She was constantly changing her mind about where to put them. It was comical to watch! You didn't need to hear what was being said because it was like watching a mime act where she would gesticulate wildly with her arms and hands flaying about in all directions. She would tell him where to dig by pointing to the spot and he would get to it, while she nodded her head in approval or, more often than not, shook her head in disapproval.

Mrs Green was very particular about her garden; everything had to be just so, with not a plant out of place or a weed to be seen between her precious rose bushes, which were naturally spaced evenly apart. Everything had to be meticulous and precise, with neat borders of plants surrounding the manicured lawn with its neatly trimmed edges. I'm surprised she didn't get Mr Green to measure everything with her dressmaking tape measure! After all, they had appearances to keep up.

Mrs Green also liked to spend time in her garden so that she could indulge in one of her favourite pastimes, which was spying on her neighbours and having a front seat on what was happening in our street. She would take ages sweeping her path and tidying up her patch of garden, just so that she could have a full view of the goings-on in our street.

I'm surprised she didn't indulge in donkey-stoning (scrubbing with an abrasive stone called a donkey stone) her front doorstep and the pavement outside her property; women engaged in this weekly practice up in the North of England. But then she wouldn't have had a good view of what was happening while her back was turned and her head bowed, on her hands and knees scrubbing the step.

However, if she had lived in one of the many terraced, back-to-back dwellings, where this donkey-stoning ritual took place, she would have been able to gossip with the other women out also donkey-stoning their steps. This weekly ritual offered women the opportunity to catch up on gossip with their neighbours.

Being outside in her front garden afforded Mrs Green a much better view than peering from behind her net curtains in her front room. She didn't appear to mind if anyone saw her, unlike me, I would rather do it more discreetly *behind* net curtains. I think she was so engrossed in watching other people that she was not aware or forgot that other people could also see her!

When she was outside her ears would prick up at the slightest sound, whenever she heard a noise in the street. She was forever darting her head to the left or right, in the direction of the sound, such as a front door opening or closing, or someone's footsteps, or the sound of a tradesman's vehicle further down the road; she would track its movements with keen interest.

It was a common sight to see visiting tradesman in the street back in the first half of the Fifties, before the convenience of fridges and freezers to store perishable food. (Perishable food was stored in what was commonly called a food or meat safe. This was a small wooden cupboard with a wire mesh screen to allow for ventilation and to keep the flies out.) Street trading was also commonplace before supermarkets and car ownership became the norm, where one could bulk buy, and transport one's shopping home.

Mrs Green's eyes were out on stalks when she had a sighting of the telegram delivery boys; they held a special attraction for her. They were, more often than not, the bearer of bad news, so she would have an inkling of what tragedy had befallen a neighbour before the unsuspecting neighbour was even aware! As soon as she realized that she had been spotted eves-dropping, she would pretend to quickly look the other way. But it took a while for the penny to drop.

Mrs Green was always gawping at other people; didn't she know it was rude to stare? She stared at me every time she saw me, but she didn't know I also stared at her. At least I had the politeness to do it when she wasn't looking! I knew what she was up to; it takes one to know one!

Mrs Green was such a nosey-parker that I think she sometimes pretended to be gardening so that she could see and hear what was going on outside in the street. She used to bend down to her conveniently low flower beds of brightly-coloured pansies and marigolds, out of sight behind the front wall of her garden, and also hide behind her privet hedge. She thought no one could spot her from these strategic positions, so she was able to listen to passers-by, or nearby neighbours gossiping.

Alternatively, she could spy on people by peering over her side fences, looking up and down the street. Or she would stand on her footpath and eavesdrop in full view by pretending to be pruning her roses or deadheading them. She always managed to emerge at the opportune time when other neighbours were out gossiping, so that she could eavesdrop or join in without necessarily being invited to do so.

She had a good excuse to be out in her front garden: she was tending her rose bushes. She was regularly watering her roses, deadheading them, and when it suited her, taking on Mr Green's job of doing weeding. This is when Mr Green had, fortunately for her, missed a few stragglers, which were threatening to invade her rose bushes.

I think Mrs Green also used her prized rose bushes as an excuse to start up a conversation with whoever crossed her path; it could have been a neighbour or even a stranger passing by. She didn't discriminate, in that instance, anyone would do, serve the purpose of being the purveyors or receivers of gossip.

She would attract passers-by first by getting them to admire her rose bushes; she would then ensnare them in conversation and would continue to hold them in conversation for ages. She was like the Venus flytrap! She was probably extracting their life history. They couldn't extricate themselves from her tentacles, as much as they might try to. It was amusing to watch, as they slowly tried to inch their way away from her all the while facing their predator, her, for fear of offending her. But she still managed to artfully keep them engaged in conversation. I would have loved to have known what they were chatting about. How I would have loved to have been a green fly on one of her rose bushes.

Mrs Green was very mindful of flying objects damaging her precious rose bushes, especially round objects, such as footballs! In those days these balls could do serious damage, as the balls were made of hard leather and therefore were very solid! These balls were responsible for breaking quite a number of window panes!

Mrs Green had taken great pleasure in confiscating these heavyweight footballs in the past. Until, Jeremy's father, the local policeman, demanded his son's ball back, informing her it was not her property, and to hand it over, which she reluctantly did! They had something in common there; like her, he also didn't like other people's children, that is, apart from his own son. (I have made a character study of Jeremy in Volume II.) Jeremy's father never seemed to mind if Mrs Green confiscated Richard's football, unless his son Jeremy happened to be playing with him at the time. (Richard is also included in my character studies in Volume II.)

Mrs Green used to constantly complain about other people's children, especially when they were playing in the street. She was always spying on children from her window, or from her front garden, watching our every move as we played our street games. After all, she, like the majority of our elders back then, believed that children should been seen and not heard. Since we had nothing of interest to impart we held no interest for her, she only viewed us as mere nuisances. If she had been a little smarter she would have realised that since we were always out and about we had plenty of juicy gossip to relate.

Unlike Mrs Green, her husband Mr Green treated us with kindness. Once, when a bunch of us children were playing in the street near his bungalow in our summer holiday from school, Mr Green very kindly brought drinks of lemon barley water out to us. He passed us each a tumbler from a tray, which he had carried out and placed on his low, front garden wall. Of course, it was like attracting bees to honey; we all congregated outside his front gate and wall to drink the welcoming, refreshing drink on what was a scorching hot August summer day. I would have liked a biscuit but didn't like to push my luck.

On another occasion, before Mr Green retired, I remember that after cycling home from work on his bike, he stopped in our street where we were all playing and gave us a packet of spangles to share. Spangles were one of the few sweets that were not strictly rationed. Of course, our elders often told us never to accept sweets from a stranger, but Mr Green wasn't a stranger to us and what's more he was trustworthy. His kind gesture naturally went down well with us being children interested in sweets, and I haven't forgotten his kindness to this day.

Mrs Green, on the other hand, behaved as if she owned the stretch of pavement and road outside her bungalow. Woe betide any children playing outside her patch, they would have to run the gauntlet with her! She didn't like anyone standing outside her property, "loitering", as she would call it, in spite of it being common practice for people to congregate out in the street back in those days.

When people met each other in the street and stopped for a chat, which they often did, and it happened to be outside her bungalow, she would be quick to break up their little tête-à-tête with a loud cough or a noise made behind their back. This quickly alerted them to her presence and they would move on further down the street. That was, if she had satiated her hunger for gossip and eavesdropping, and didn't want to join in.

When it was inclement weather Mrs Green contented herself with staring out of her front window into the street, watching us children with her beady eyes. She thought nobody could see her standing or sitting at her window because she had net curtains to shield her from view. She had also cleverly, she thought, lined up a few strategically placed potted plants along the window sill to prevent anyone from seeing her. But she failed to comprehend that any passer-by could still make out her head bobbing up and down in-between the potted plants, if they were close enough. Or when she had her head close enough to the window, almost pressed against it! And if it was sunny, one could detect her shadow from the reflection of the sun's rays on her window. I didn't understand the logic, especially when she didn't mind if people saw her in full view when she stood in her front garden openly staring.

Mrs Green was such a hypocrite. Despite not liking other people, including us children "loitering" outside her property, she would be quite happy to stand outside other neighbours' properties to have a chat when she felt like it. This was a regular occurrence: Mr and Mrs Green often went out for an evening stroll along our street, in common with other neighbours, if the weather was pleasant enough. So Mrs Green had no need of a dog as an excuse to go for a walk. This was of course, before television arrived in our street around the time of the Queen's Coronation in June, 1953. The TV tended to keep everyone indoors.

Mrs Green resisted getting a television set for as long as possible, even though neighbours had heard Mr Green was keen. She naturally didn't want to curtail her favourite pastime, of being nosey on other people's patches when out on her evening jaunts! Until, that is, she cottoned on that she would have a much broader scope to be nosey in other people's lives, and what was generally going on in other parts of the world, via the television.

One programme in particular that kept her inside in the evening, once they became the proud owners of a television, was Britain's first television soap opera series 'The Grove Family'. It was a long running series and a live production, which first aired in April, 1954 (ending in June, 1957). The storyline revolved around the daily lives of a typical, extended family, consisting of parents, their children and a grandmother, who all lived under one roof. This human drama captivated viewers, as it did, Mrs Green. I heard she wouldn't miss an episode of this very popular series, which I suspect, must have been much to Mr Green's relief, as he wasn't forced to accompany her on her night-time vigils.

Of course, during the day Mrs Green would also satisfy her desire for gossip by listening to popular dramas on the radio. One such drama popular with listening audiences, and probably also popular with Mrs Green, was '*Mrs Dale's Diary*'. This BBC Light Programme first aired on the radio in 1948. It was on daily at 4pm every weekday afternoon and repeated the following morning.

This radio drama concerned the daily goings-on in a suburb of London, (which would be right up Mrs Green's street)! It featured a doctor's family, as relayed in the diary of the doctor's wife, Mrs Dale (played by Ellis Powell). Mrs Dale was constantly troubled about her doctor husband Jim, expressed in her oft heard phrase, "I'm rather worried about Jim". This provided the central theme for the storylines and became a catchphrase with the listening audience.

Another popular serialised drama on the radio was '*The Archers*'. This would keep Mrs Green inside her home, for a short while a least, to listen to the evening broadcasts: '*The Archers*' was only on for fifteen minutes every weekday evening. It first aired nationwide on 1st, January, 1951. (Pilot episodes were broadcast on the BBC's Midlands Home Service during the Spring Bank Holiday commencing 29th May, 1950.) '*The Archers*' now takes credit for being the world's longest running radio serial drama, which is still being broadcast! The drama takes place on a farm and was advertised as, "A tale of everyday country folk", which would naturally appeal to Mrs Green's nosiness.

As well as being a drama depicting the goings-on in a rural village, '*The Archers*' was also meant to be educational for farmers. To this end, it featured matters of a rural nature; (the producer, Godfrey Baseley had apparently mainly specialised in producing agricultural programmes). Farming methods were especially important at a time when the population relied on the land for food with the rationing of many foodstuffs still in place and limited food imports. This is why this radio drama probably also appealed to Mr Green. His excuse for listening to it was that it would help him with his production of food from their little allotment in their back garden. Of course, Mrs Green probably got him to undertake daily chores whilst listening to this radio serial, since it wasn't like the television where you had to listen as well as watch the little box in the corner.

Prior to Mrs Green acquiring a television however, she continued her regular evening stroll, with Mr Green in attendance. When Mrs Green was out and about on the prowl this gave her another opportunity to be nosey by peering into other people's windows, which she had a habit of doing. Her view through other people's windows was often restricted though, in the darker nights of autumn and winter because residents had closed their curtains. But occasionally, she came across someone who had not yet closed their curtains. And with the light on, she was in seventh heaven, as she had a much clearer view through net curtains of a lit room than she would have had in natural daylight.

On their evening walks Mrs Green always appeared eager to stop to chat to any passers-by. She would open a conversation with the cliché "Good Evening." And Mr Green would doff (raise) his cap as a matter of courtesy. Often these people were neighbours, but she also met strangers who had strayed from their usual patches. That's probably where Mr and Mrs Green disappeared in the evenings: exploring unchartered territory. This provided a hotbed for gossip with new, unsuspecting residents out walking also. After all, she didn't want to confine herself to our street, when taking an evening stroll was the done thing back then in the early Fifties without the distraction of the television.

I often wondered what on earth Mrs Green could find to talk about with strangers. But every time I saw her, she always managed to engage the other solitary person or couple in our street; both she and Mr Green spent quite a considerable time standing in our street chatting to them. Mrs Green would take the lead in the conversation. I would see her gesturing non-stop with her hands as she talked, while her husband just stood there silently smiling, as his attempts at small talk, I expect, were limited. He couldn't have had much practice. Mrs Green had the disagreeable habit of not allowing Mr Green to get a word in edgeways before she would interrupt him, by speaking over the top of him. If the stranger had a dog, all the better, as far as Mr Green was concerned; it gave him an opportunity to preoccupy himself with patting the dog, rather than looking around embarrassed, while his wife stood there gossiping. Jawing', was the slang word sometimes used.

Waiting in shop queues, which was a common feature of everyday life for housewives in the post-war years, as it had been in the war years, gave Mrs Green another opportunity to gossip to her heart's content. Queuing with the rest of the housewives outside the various shops whilst waiting for their rationed goods and other commodities that were in short supply provided Mrs

Green with the perfect stomping ground for gossip. There would be the baker, butcher, fishmonger, grocer, greengrocer, newsagent/tobacconist and confectioner. Including an ironmonger (seller of hardware), cobbler (shoe repairer) and the haberdasher (seller of sewing merchandise), all providing ample opportunity for Mrs Green to linger and thus prolong her gossipmongering.

Mrs Green enjoyed the ritual of doing her shopping at individual shops, as it gave her the opportunity to gossip to the shop owner and their helpers, and the other customers at each of these shops. However, the demise of the individual shops in favour of the new self-service styled supermarket must have come as an unwelcome development for Mrs Green. She must have viewed this progress as a step too far, since it would limit her opportunity for gossiping to just one shop!

Self-service shops had been in existence with some of the cooperative shops (co-ops) since the Forties, whereby individual grocers operated out of one shop. However, J. Sainsbury, a long established grocery shop, claims credit for being the first grocer to sell a range of different grocery products and household wares in their first self-service styled supermarket. It opened in Croydon, a Borough of South London, on 26th June, 1950. As the idea caught on, the introduction of self-service styled supermarkets opened in other towns up and down the country.

The new self service shop meant that customers could do their entire shopping, under one roof. Gone were the days of chatting with each individual shopkeeper. Having a conversation with the other customers and the shopkeepers and their assistants in each shop, whilst waiting for your items to be brought to you and wrapped by them, was no longer possible with self-service. The customer now undertook the job formerly done by the shopkeeper and their assistants. After placing all their items selected by them in their wire basket, the customer simply paid the till cashier at the checkout counter before exiting the shop.

On the opening day of the first self-service Sainsbury store in Croydon, it was reported that one middle-class, female customer on being presented with a wire basket by the owner Mr J. Sainsbury, was so disgusted with the concept of serving herself that she slung it back at him in disgust! (If she wanted to be waited on, perhaps she should have stayed at home and relied on home deliveries; the better off still enjoyed special weekly deliveries of the food they ordered from the grocer and the greengrocer, among other suppliers.)

Some customers, like the one described, probably disapproved of the loss of deference that came with counter service. Another disadvantage for some was the lack of personal service and social interaction, which meant that there was nobody to have a conversation with, apart from other customers waiting in a queue at the till point.

When all rationing ceased on 4th July, 1954, Mrs Green's delight must have also been tinged with disappointment; the disappearance of the extra long queues in shops, which rationing and the scarcity of goods caused, curtailed her gossiping. She would have to find other sources where she could pick up gossip.

The local hairdressing salon provided Mrs Green with another fertile place for gossipmongering; though, I hasten to add, not during wartime, as these establishments were obviously thin on the ground. Mrs Green, along with most women, had a difficult job on her hands to look after her hair during wartime when shampoos were hard to come by, and even water was rationed! Soap was also rationed. She could of course, have sprinkled that old stalwart, talc on her scalp and combed it through her hair to remove any dirt and residue of grease. Whilst vinegar, a multi-purpose household cleaning product would make her hair look and feel squeaky clean.

Mrs Green probably resorted to wearing a turban to cover her hair, as most women did, especially during the war. Women working in factories during the war wore turbans; it prevented their hair from getting caught up in dangerous factory machinery. Turbans not only helped to protect the hair from dirt and dust but also helped to keep it clean in-between washes. Looking after her own hair at home must have starved Mrs Green of gossip.

Once the war was over however, women were able to indulge in a regular trip to a hairdressing salon to maintain the fashionable short, curly style that was in vogue in the early Fifties with both the young and old. The 'poodle cut' (so named because the permed, tight curls piled on top of the head resemble the curly coat of a poodle dog), was particularly favoured among older women, as it had been in the Forties. Famous exponents of the poodle cut were the American actresses Betty Grable and Lucille Ball.

Indeed, it was probably due to the poodle cut and to the short curly style in general that led to the proliferation of hairdressing salons in Britain in the Fifties. These salons catered for a women's pride in her appearance, which was high on the agenda of a woman in the Fifties, where a regular shampoo and set helped to maintain the desired neat and tidy look.

Mrs Green must have looked forward to the luxury of her often weekly or sometimes fortnightly visit to the hairdressers, as it also gave her an opportunity for a gossip with the other patrons and with the hairdresser. It was the one place where she could legitimately spend several hours sitting there gossiping because she was having her hair done.

Since most of the women in our neighbourhood congregated at the hairdressers, it provided a hotbed for gossip. There, she could find out what was going on in the neighbourhood: where, when, and with whom. It must have been like a British Housewives' League meeting in the salon, where in common with those ladies, they probably also discussed the unfairness of food rationing, among other hot topics of the day.

The, British Housewives' League, was a women's protest movement. It was set up by a London vicar's wife, Mrs Iris Lovelock, in June, 1945, initially in response to the meat ration, which had been reimposed after the war had ended. The movement captured the mood of housewives' frustrations at having to endure rations and hardships that continued long after the war.

Mrs Green enjoyed spending the good part of Saturday morning in the hairdressing salon having her hair coiffured for the weekend, especially for church on Sunday. I would often see her enter and exit the hairdressers on a Saturday in the local high street.

I would also spot her through the hairdresser's window when I walked past. She would be typically gossiping to the woman customer sat next to her in the neighbouring chair, while they both waited their turn to have their hair shampooed and set. Then again, when she was having her short, mousy, greying hair twisted into tight rollers by the hairdresser, which looked quite a painful process. And later, when she had her hair styled by the hairdresser, it gave her another opportunity to also talk to the hairdressers, who were usually very chatty. I bet she picked up lots of snippets of gossip in the hairdressing salon.

The only time when she couldn't gossip was when she had to sit for hours on end waiting for the curls to set and dry under those large, voluminous hood hairdryers, which lined the walls of every hairdressing salon. These dryers were far too noisy, which prevented Mrs Green from being able to hear what was being said. So she had to content herself with spending the rest of her time under the dryer reading all the women's magazines: '*Good Housekeeping*', '*Woman*', '*Woman's Own*', and '*Women's Weekly*'.

These weekly magazines ('*Good Housekeeping*' was, and still is, a monthly publication), provided a source of gossip but of the more tame variety, providing general advice for women, and tips on how to maintain their homes and themselves with articles on the home, fashion, hair and beauty. I bet she much preferred to get her hands on the weekly copy of, '*Titbits*', which was more up her street with its mix of news items, especially its sensationalist human dramas!

* * *

When Mrs Green wasn't being a noisy parker and a gossip she liked to be the focal point of the gossip. She enjoyed being the centre of attention. Becoming one of the first neighbours in our street to be the proud owners of a motor car she certainly achieved this aim, along with her husband, although he was a modest man by nature.

I wondered how they could afford to buy a car, as it wasn't second-hand: Mrs Green made sure everyone in the neighbourhood was left in no doubt about it being a brand new car. There had been gossip in the street that either he or she had been left a small family inheritance, which enabled them to splash out on a car. But more than likely, like the lucky few, Mr and Mrs Green had probably been saving up for several years to buy their first car.

There was at least a twelve month to a two year waiting list for a car, as production was limited due to shortage of raw materials, which were used on rearmament. Most cars that were produced were for export to help our country's economic recovery after the war. The car naturally became a status symbol to those lucky enough to own one.

When Mr and Mrs Green finally became the proud owners of a Morris Minor two-door, mid-green coloured saloon car, Mrs Green liked nothing better than showing it off to all the neighbours. The designer of the Morris Minor was Alec Issigonis; this distinctive car's launch in September, 1948, was at the British Motor Show at Earls Court, London. This affordable model for the average man in the street went on to become Britain's first best selling car.

(Mr Issigonis later went on to design the smaller Mini, launched under the names, Morris Mini-Minor and the Austin Seven; Mr Issigonis introduced both models to Britain in August, 1959. These two cars were eventually renamed the MINI and went on to become another of Britain's best selling cars from the Sixties onwards; it was an iconic car with a cult following, like the Morris Minor.)

I think Mr and Mrs Green's Morris Minor was more to impress the neighbours than anything else, since they didn't use it that much, except at weekends. They only used the car for short but necessary journeys, such as for church and to see relatives out of town. The cost of running it must have been prohibitive, especially when petrol was expensive and had been on ration prior to 26th May, 1950 when it was derationed.

When, the government rationed petrol they brought in a new law, the Motor Spirit (Regulations) Act 1948, in which a red dye was introduced to petrol for commercial use only. The aim of this measure was to prevent private motorists from supplementing their rationed petrol for personal use. It was also used as a deterrent to the black market trade in petrol. Of course, Mr Green wasn't the sort to try and deceive the system by circumventing the law as some did. There were reports that some unscrupulous private motorists had resorted to straining the red dye through a gas mask left over from the war, or through a sieve, or even through a loaf of bread!

The couple kept their beloved Morris Minor in the garage and brought it out at the weekend. That's when Mr Green took Mrs Green for a spin (after petrol had come off ration), perhaps for an occasional drive out into the countryside; this was a popular leisure pursuit back in the first half of the Fifties, before the introduction of foreign travel in the latter half of the decade.

People yearned to get away from it all and escape from the town into the quiet and peaceful countryside. Travelling by bicycle, bus and train were the most common forms of transport back then. Mr and Mrs Green were therefore fortunate in that they both had the convenience and luxury of being able to travel further afield in their own private car. Of course, they also used their car for their obligatory attendance at our local church on Sunday.

With the imposition of petrol rationing, Mr Green had to be content with driving his car out of the garage only, where it would remain stationary. He just wanted to admire and clean it and ensure it was in tip-top condition and raring to go when petrol finally came off ration, which it did not long after, during the Whitsun holiday in May, 1950.

Mr Green treated his car as if it were his child! It was his pride and joy. He handled it with loving care like it was his most precious possession. He lavished attention on it. I used to see him cleaning it every weekend on a Saturday before church on Sunday morning. He would drive his car out of their specially, newly built garage and clean and polish it with a deep sense of satisfaction. He always kept it looking spic and span. He would spend hours on its maintenance, that was, when he was given permission to by his spouse.

I think Mr Green also viewed the car as a means of escape from Mrs Green's constant bickering, since he had a good excuse, which was to spend time on keeping it in excellent condition. He carried out all his spot checks to ensure that everything was in good working order: the tyres, the mirrors, the lights, including the little winged indicator lights. These distinctive trafficators (semaphore signals) stuck out on either side of the car looking like little wings when he indicated he was turning left or right, which I always found amusing. He also checked under the bonnet, the oil and the water levels.

Mr Green would then be keen to start the car engine up, ever wary of making too much noise, which would bring his spouse rushing outside to admonish him in front of the neighbours for making such a din. He was therefore careful to rev the engine gently so it purred softly enough to let him know everything was ticking over nicely; ready for use, as the all important Sunday outing to church approached.

I enjoyed watching Mr Green giving his car a thorough wash every weekend with a pail of water and a sponge, lathering it with lots of soap suds, when soap came off ration, that is, in September, 1950. Then he would rinse it with a sponge and a pail of clean water, before finally giving it a polish to a gleaming shine so that he could see his reflection in it.

While he cleaned and polished his car, I bet Mr Green was probably dreaming of the weekend drive, which was not too far away, when he could drive his beloved car, as this was the only time when he was in charge. Mrs Green couldn't drive so this was the one time when Mr Green felt in command. Driving allowed Mr Green to be in the driving seat for once. He must have enjoyed this role of taking control and being in charge, which was so foreign to him. It gave him an opportunity to put his wife in her place because she had to rely on him being in charge for a change. Until that is, Mrs Green disturbed Mr Green's pleasant daydream by opening the front window of their bungalow to call him in, as he had spent enough time on the car, and she had other household chores lined up for him to do.

When Mr Green was not cleaning or tinkering with his beloved car, he was forever talking about it. He would talk for ages on his car and its inner workings with admiring male neighbours or whoever was willing to listen, when he got the chance. It was the same with football, and when it was the season for cricket.

Mr Green, in common with most of the male population back in the fifties, was a keen football spectator, attending the local football matches when he was allowed to attend by his wife. He also used to listen to the football broadcasts on the radio; both would be followed by a post-mortem after the match with the other men folk. One such football match broadcast live on the radio was the much talked about 1953, FA (Football Association) Cup Final, held the month before the Coronation, on 2nd May. It took place at the Wembley stadium in London.

Also much talked about was its star player Stanley Mathews, who became famous for helping Blackpool to win the Cup, beating Bolton Wanderers: the winning score was four goals to three. Stan Mortensen scored a hat-trick and Bill Perry scored the winning goal for Blackpool. I overheard Mr Green enthusiastically discussing this memorable match with some neighbours, until that is, his spouse rudely interrupted him and told him to stop talking and attend to other things that needed his attention.

I always made a habit of looking out for Mr and Mrs Green on Sundays, at the allotted time when they used their car for church. Their life seemed to revolve around the weekly Sunday visit to church.

* * *

In common with the majority of the population and certainly our neighbourhood back in those days, Mr and Mrs Green were regular churchgoers. They belonged to the Anglican Church of England, as a lot of families did, including mine. (Although, I understand that there were a higher percentage of Roman Catholics compared to Protestants who attended church back then.)

Mr and Mrs Green never missed church on Sunday, like most people in the early Fifties, and if they did, it would have been a rare occurrence. Their attendance, like the majority of churchgoers back in the early part of the decade, was as regular and punctual as clockwork.

I couldn't understand everyone's keenness to attend church, apart from habit. I, as a child, found church services dull, boring and a waste of time (except for Reverend Wheatcroft's sermons.) I detested even more, Sunday school! I didn't want yet more schooling; I had had enough of that all week! Sunday was supposed to be a day of rest, especially after a busy week at school! Not much chance of that though. But like most children we were sent to Sunday school as a matter of course.

At Sunday school they even had the temerity to set us homework, which I never did. The most daring of our group, such as Richard, my next door neighbour, and I, made every attempt to get out of Sunday school by disappearing when no one was looking, and going to play in forbidden areas outside in the fields behind the church hall. I don't think we were ever missed, surprisingly. Or perhaps nothing was said by the Sunday school teacher because we were too troublesome to teach!

Mr and Mrs Green looked all important when they went to church every Sunday morning, dressed in their Sunday best. I always had an opportunity to see them because they always went to church earlier than everyone else. Mr Green was one of the bell-ringers and therefore had to ring before the beginning of the service to call everyone to prayer, while Mrs Green checked the church's floral display, which she was in charge of.

Mrs Green would parade herself on her front path, waiting for Mr Green to drive their prized Morris Minor carefully out of the garage. This gave Mrs Green ample time to check that her attire was all spic and span. She would pat down any creases in her matching twin-piece, costumed black jacket and knee length skirt and readjust her black, small, close fitting 'half hat', which sat comfortably perched on top of her coiffured head.

Mr Green would be wearing his smart but worn dark suit. It was not unusual for people, in particular men, to wear the same suit until it wore out, due to the scarcity of cloth during and after the war. In fact, younger men who had served in the Second World War were issued with a demob suit on their return to Civvy Street, which was usually the only suit they owned.

Topping off Mr Green's suit would be the ubiquitous trilby hat. However, he would have to remove his hat as a mark of respect before entering church and whilst attending church services.

While Mrs Green awaited Mr Green and their car, it also gave her an opportunity to pull on her tight-fitting black gloves and wiggle her fingers in them so they were a snug fit. Her small, black boxed, neat handbag would hang suspended from her raised arm.

Probably, contained within her handbag was a donation of some coins for the church collection plate; together with a handkerchief for when she felt moved enough by the sermon to shed a tear. While in one gloved hand she clutched her personal copy of the '*Book of Common Prayer*' close to her chest so that any onlookers were left in no doubt where she was heading. Hoping all the while that the neighbours had sufficient time to see and admire her smart apparel.

Mrs Green's husband was at her beck and call, as usual. She would wait while he ran round to her side and opened the car door for her, ensuring also that the neighbours had ample time to observe her looking her best. Mr Green would then take hold of her handbag and wait patiently for her to get in with the maximum of decorum; after ensuring she was sitting comfortably, he would then close her door, after first placing her handbag on the back seat. Mr Green's performance was worthy of a round of applause, as his wife was perfectly capable of opening the car door herself. Although, it has to be said, that men behaved like true gentlemen in those days and chivalrously opened doors for ladies.

While Mrs Green waited for Mr Green to return to his side of the car and get in and start up the motor she would use the opportunity to remove her vanity mirror out of the glove compartment. She would then check once more her face, and tweak her hair to ensure it was set in place. Then she would wait impatiently for him to drive off down the road.

When they drove off, I half expected Mrs Green to give a regal wave from the window to any neighbours who, like me, were watching the show. Just like the newly crowned Queen Elizabeth, who I had seen in lots of pictures, waved to the crowds of onlookers from her royal carriage, the Gold State Coach, on her way to Westminster Abbey to be crowned Queen on her Coronation day.

Mr and Mrs Green often gave a lift to an elderly lady attending church who lived in the same street as us. She was made to feel like royalty as she stepped inside their car. Since it was only a two-door saloon Mr Green was obliged to tip the front seat forward so the elderly lady could clamber onto the back seat, which was rather undignified at her old age! But she wasn't about to complain, as it was preferable to getting on the bus or walking, especially if it rained. Mrs Green was certainly not going to be usurped from her front seat, as it gave her status; not only could onlookers clearly see her, but sitting in the front commanded the best view.

The Sunday church service was the most important highlight of Mrs Green's week. Attending church ensured that she was: "spiritually fed for the week so that she could carry on gossiping about the neighbours with impunity", so my mother said.

Strangely, Mrs Green thought it was acceptable to spread malicious gossip about people during the rest of the week. She was often heard to exclaim, "Did you hear about so and so?" And, "Have you heard the latest?" Then she would take the person to whom she was confiding in aside and fill them in on all the salacious details. Mrs Green would always be the first person to cast the first stone, and cast aspersions on her neighbours. She was also very quick to heap criticism on everyone else but herself, because of course, she was above reproach; she was not only a regular churchgoer but also did good deeds for the church in her voluntary capacity, which purified her of sin and any wrongdoing. She was such a hypocrite!

If Mrs Green felt so inclined, she would believe by attending church she was also serving her penance for any minor transgressions or misdemeanours; these would be forgiven, as in church she could cleanse herself of all her sins when taking the Holy Communion. She therefore attended church with a clear conscience. I always used to think her long suffering spouse deserved a few prayers said in church especially for him for putting up with her for all those years.

Being a volunteer at her local church gave Mrs Green the chance not only to redeem herself but also another chance to chatter and gossip with the other women folk who were also church volunteers.

Mrs Green thought by also undertaking voluntary work at the church, she was one of the chosen few; it gave her a special standing in the community, it gave her VIP status. After all, she did more than most in her commitment to the church, which meant she was a person that should be held in high regard, and so should be above criticism from lesser mortals. In God's eyes she had done her good deed for the week: fulfilled her voluntary duties; attended church; taken Holy Communion, and to boot, given generously to the church funds when the collection plate was passed round.

There was gossip circulating that every time the collection plate was passed to Mrs Green she would take her time removing money out of her purse, so that all eyes were on her. She would then make sure that the coins rattled loudly onto the plate so that parishioners were left in no doubt as to how generous she was.

Mr Green enjoyed indulging in the ancient craft of bell-ringing at our church. He had taken up bell-ringing again with renewed enthusiasm, after it had been discontinued during the war. (The bells also fell silent during the Great War of 1914-1918.)

Mr Green was no doubt, eternally grateful that our old church retained several of its ancient features. This included a rectangular tower that housed the bells, which allowed him an escape route from his spouse.

Our church had a relatively large tower housing ten bells. So he was spoilt for choice. He could practice and ring on each of them, from the number one, 'treble', the smallest and lightest bell, to the number ten, 'tenor', the heaviest and loudest sounding bell: some churches have only four bells!

Bell-ringing practice provided Mr Green with a good excuse to spend time away from his spouse, just like fishing, his allotment, potting shed, and of course, the cinema did. But he also enjoyed the companionship provided by bell-ringing with like-minded people, which appeared to be absent from his relationship with his wife.

As well as regular outings to other towers, bell-ringing practice took place locally at our church, every Thursday evening for a couple of hours. Mr Green would also ensure that he stayed behind to tie up the bells.

We neighbours could hear in our street, the bell-ringers practicing in church, if the wind blew in the right direction. From ringing simple 'rounds', which are rung in sequence starting from the smallest to the heaviest bell, to 'change ringing', which alters the 'rounds', with a method, such as, 'Plain Bob', or more complicated change ringing methods. These always depend on how many bell-ringers are present, which in turn dictates how many bells they can ring on.

If the Ringing Master had a full team in our church then they could ring the method, 'Grandsire Royal', or 'Stedman Royal'; the latter name in a method usually stipulates how many bells are being rung in the method. According to Mr Green, a method rang on *ten* bells is called 'Royal'. He would talk enthusiastically on the art of bell-ringing whenever he got the chance; this is why I've retained a lot of information on the topic.

Mr Green was eternally grateful for the fact that his short but stout wife didn't have the stamina to ring the bells, let alone be able to climb the never-ending, winding, steep, stone steps up to the ringing chamber! (He didn't let on that there were boxes to stand on if a ringer was short in height and couldn't reach the ropes unaided.) Thus he was able to escape from her constant bickering. The ringing chamber is situated below the belfry, which houses the bells at the top of the tower.

I heard Mr Green also used to frighten his wife, which was no easy feat, with horror stories of what could befall a bell-ringer if he or she wasn't paying due care and attention. There had been cases where a bell-ringer had been lifted off their feet and landed up in the belfry, sustaining injuries or worse!

The hazards of bell-ringing also involve the complex apparatus, which pertains to the practice of bell-ringing. Certain mechanisms, such as the, 'stay', which is part of the frame housing the bell can be broken if the ropes aren't handled with due care, and these are expensive to replace.

Due to the hazards and dangers entailed in bell-ringing, every bell-ringer has to adhere to stringent rules and regulations Mr Green was quick to inform his wife, so I heard. He must have told her, as he did us children, that bell-ringing always begins with the 'lead' treble bell-ringer alerting the other bell-ringers that he or she is about to start the ringing by calling out "Stand to! The treble's going, she's gone!" The conductor would also call "Stand!" at the end of a bell-ringing session; this meant that everyone had to stop ringing. I suspect that Mrs Green didn't want to conform by toeing the line. She was used to giving the orders. These stories, among others, were enough to deter Mrs Green from ever entertaining the idea of entering the ringing chamber to join them.

Mr Green was also grateful for the fact that bell ringers seemed to have their own language. 'Campanologists', as they are called, talk in a strange vernacular that Mrs Green would find difficult to decipher. It meant for once she couldn't partake in conversations.

Campanologists talked of holding the 'tail end', or the 'sally'. This is the usually striped red, white and blue twisted, fluffy rope end that the ringers grip hold of in order to pull the respective bells down to do what's called a, 'hand-stroke', and alternatively, the 'back-stroke', when the bells go up. (I recall seeing these distinctive ropes hanging in the ringing chamber, when I was shown up the tower once.)

Bell-ringers discussed ringing 'rounds', and 'changes', with a 'call' for a slight alteration, called a 'bob', a 'single', or a 'touch'. Manoeuvres were referred to as, 'dodging' and 'hunting', and 'hunting-up' and 'hunting-down'.

Campanologists rang 'methods', of which there are many, with odd names. These 'methods' are also often complicated to understand, with even 'surprise' methods thrown in to complicate matters further! I expect it would have all been above Mrs Green's head!

Mr Green would often delight in saying to his wife: "They're a bell-ringer short!" This meant that a neighbouring church, which had a bell tower, needed another bell-ringer to complete their team, and this would often be, again, much to his delight, at short notice. This request, which he heard on the grapevine, by word of mouth, made Mr Green's day, as it would mean that he could escape from household duties for a while. The bells would only need to be rung for around twenty minutes to half an hour but it entailed travelling to and from the church by bicycle, as he would never be allowed to take the car when petrol was at a premium; this meant that he could be gone for an hour or two, if he dragged his feet.

He would also eagerly take part in bell striking competitions representing our county, Essex, which would take up even more of his time. He liked to participate, whenever possible, in a 'quarter-peal', or better still, a 'peal', as it consisted of around five thousand bell changes (bell pulls or rings) and took about three hours or more to ring!

He also had the obligatory Sunday service to ring for before the morning Eucharist service started and then later for the evensong service in the evening. Then of course, there were the most important calendar events in a parishioner's life: baptisms and weddings.

For funerals, the bells would be muffled to deaden (no pun intended) the sound. Everyone living in the early Fifties will remember the sombre occasion of the then Princess Elizabeth's, father, King George the Sixth's death, on 6th February, 1952 and the state of mourning that followed: muffled bells were rung from churches throughout the land. The bells rang again for the funeral, on 30th March, 1953, of Queen Mary, the mother of the late King George the Sixth, and the widow of King George the Fifth. Mr Green was always counted on to ring for such occasions.

It is said he rang after the declaration of the ending of the Second World War, as did every bell tower in the country. The bells rang out informing inhabitants of the ending of the war and as celebration of this fact. (The bells, although silenced during the war, would only ring to warn the population of an enemy invasion.)

More recently, Mr Green rang to celebrate on 2nd June, 1953, the happy occasion of the Coronation of Queen Elizabeth the Second. Mr Green participated in this celebration with great enthusiasm, when the bells rang out once more, making a joyous sound from every bell tower in the land.

I would overhear Mr Green trying to explain the technique of bell-ringing to anyone that would listen. According to Mr Green, bell-ringing required the ringer to possess multi-skills. Bell-ringing methods consist of complicated mathematical permutations, which the bell ringer would have to work out while attempting to strike the bell in time. So you need to be not only good with numbers but also quick thinking on your feet. You also need to possess good rope sighting skills, in order to observe the positions of all the ropes, so you can ring in time sequence. Also, good listening skills are required in order to hear the striking of the other bells. You also need to have excellent concentration! As far as Mrs Green was concerned it probably all sounded too exhausting!

Mr Green tried to educate us children in the pleasures of bell ringing. Even if Mrs Green showed no interest, I was determined to master the techniques of bell- ringing, as Mr Green described them to us, when I was older and my levels of concentration were more focused for the task in hand.

There was a rumour going round that Mrs Green wanted Mr Green to put his name down to become a churchwarden. However, he was supposed to have said he couldn't possibly have done it to the best of his ability if he was to fulfil his important role of bell-ringing. He much preferred bell-ringing, of course, as being up in the tower ringing bells he was able to break free from his wife. Becoming a churchwarden would have meant that he would have been working closely with her breathing down his neck while she went about her own voluntary duties in the church.

While Mr Green concentrated his efforts on bell-ringing, Mrs Green concentrated her efforts on the general housekeeping in our church, which included organising the flower arranging. This meant that more often than not, she bossed the other flower arrangers by instructing them on how best they should go about arranging the flowers.

Flowers need constant watering in order to stay fresh. Floral (florist) foam that had water absorbing sponge-like properties, helped flower arrangers with the watering process; it was invented in 1954, by a company in the United States, called Smithers-Oasis. Oases provided a boon to flower arrangers and florists alike: the water holding foam structure helps to preserve the flowers and the foam also helps to support the flower arrangement; its resin, rigid, foam structure holds the flowers in place. Unfortunately, for our ladies, I suspect they had to wait a while longer for this revolutionary product to reach Britain.

Mrs Green would also generally give her orders on the undertaking of other chores of a household nature, in the church.

All the women took it in turns to dust and polish the wooden pews where the congregation sit in the nave in the main area of the church at the west end. But Mrs Green always managed to reserve what she considered the best or more important chores for herself! She made sure that she always got to dust and polish the place reserved for the clergy and the choir, called the chancel, which by three low steps separates the clergy and the choir from the congregation seated below in the nave. It gave her an exalted feeling of power.

She also took a keen interest in the vestry (sacristy) because it is where the clergy's official robes 'vestments' and liturgical items are kept, and it also serves as an office where parochial business takes place. But she was especially interested in polishing the pulpit, which is usually, a wood or stone hexagonal structure, situated high above the nave, reached discreetly by a series of winding steps at the side.

The pulpit is, of course, the place where the vicar stands towering over the congregation, to deliver his Sunday sermon. Mrs Green liked to imagine on Sundays when she joined the ordinary congregation seated on the pews down in the nave that she had been privy to that special place high up in the raised platformed pulpit, on the left side of the church, reserved for the vicar.

The lectern, (a tall stand with a sloping top), also held a special fascination for Mrs Green; it is where the vicar reads from the huge gilt bound Holy Bible that rests open on it at the appropriate passage for that Sunday's service. Mrs Green therefore paid special attention to this brass lectern, with regard to her polishing duties.

I understand that Anglican Church lecterns stand on the right side of the church, and like at our church, are usually in the shape of an eagle standing on a ball. Mrs Green was only too aware that the eagle was a powerful, spiritual symbol of the divine.

The eagle represents Saint John the Evangelist (an Apostle and the writer of one of the four gospels); since it soars higher and thus closer to God than any other bird and is capable of seeing far and wide. The eagle is therefore the perfect vehicle to spread the gospel, represented by the open Bible resting on its back and outstretched wings. It carries God's message throughout the church, and also to the four corners of the earth, which is symbolised by the sphere that it stands on. Mrs Green ensured that she had also left her scent of beeswax wafting in the air for the eagle to carry with it on its journey.

She also made it known that she was allowed access to the holiest part of the church, the sanctuary, situated at the east end of the church. There she polished the alter table and arranged the flowers on it. But I don't know whether this was true because I heard women were not allowed in the holiest part of the church, in the sanctuary area.

Mrs Green was also a member of the Women's Institute, commonly referred to as the WI. The Women's Institute had many members in the Fifties. Our local branch held their meetings in the church hall, as many branches did.

Mrs Green held a position on the WI committee, which gave her an elevated feeling of self-importance. Since she enjoyed bossing people about when she wasn't bossing Mr Green, having a position on the committee suited her down to the ground. She also enjoyed talking and listening to the sound of her own voice. The WI, in addition, provided another rich source for local gossip. Mrs Green was branch secretary so she had all the member's personal details, which satisfied her nosiness.

Mrs Green also took great pleasure in helping to organise the church's religious festivals in the Christian calendar, by organising the refreshments. She would host with the other ladies of the WI the Easter festivities; summer fetes, fairs and church bazaars; the harvest festival, and the Christmas festivities, which, of course, included organising all the flower arranging.

She always reserved a special seat for our vicar, Reverend Wheatcroft, when he attended without fail, afternoon tea at fetes and the like. The church events organisers held these either in Reverend Wheatcroft's vicarage garden or in the adjacent church hall if the weather was inclement. Whenever Mrs Green spied Reverend Wheatcroft, at one of the many church functions, she would make a beeline for him and collar him before he had a chance to escape. She liked to think she was in cahoots with the vicar.

She would then insist that Reverend Wheatcroft have some more cake, which he was always slow to refuse: she knew food, and in particular cake, was his Achilles heel. He then had to listen to her, which was a small price to pay, while he indulged in one of his favourite past-times: eating and drinking.

(Reverend Wheatcroft was such a fascinating character who was intimately involved in the lives of the residents of our street that I have naturally included him in my character studies; a lot of what we learnt about him was gleaned from his good-natured but gossipy housekeeper.)

* * *

I still used to see Mr and Mrs Green going about their daily activities towards the end of the middle Fifties. I suspected things were much the same in the couple's bungalow, as they had always been. Each of them had their own pursuits, which allowed them, in particular Mr Green, time to themselves, so they both lived their separate lives in a way, but were living under the same roof.

The introduction of more affordable labour-saving gadgets on the market as the decade progressed would free Mrs Green from domestic chores; it would also allow her more time to gossip with the neighbours.

There was the indispensable Kenwood food mixer, introduced by Ken Wood (hence the product name) onto the market in 1950. The first heat-controlled steam iron was introduced by Morphy Richards in 1954. Meanwhile, the Hoover Company were continuing to make developments to their vacuum cleaners. Later in the decade, a single tub or twin-tub washing machine (one tub for washing, the other for spin-drying), were the must-have products on the market, as was, in the following decade, a domestic refrigerator.

Such innovative products as these were too expensive in the first half of the Fifties for the average consumer. However, all this labour-saving technology, would in the near future, allow Mrs Green more free time to spend outside the home gossiping and sticking her nose into other people's business.

Mr Green tried not to step on Mrs Green's toes but allowed her to step on his; it made for a marriage of convenience, if nothing else. They were both now too long in the tooth to change their living arrangements. Besides, divorce, although rising to its highest level in the immediate post-war period, which peaked in 1947, was still almost unheard of back then. On the relatively rare occasion when divorce did happen, it was frowned upon. Being church people Mr and Mrs Green, like most married couples, learnt to put on a brave face to the outside world.

126

A Young, Newly Married Couple Who Lodged Nearby With Their Landlady Mrs Trenchard

I used to observe with interest a newly married, young couple who lived nearby at number thirty. They rented two furnished rooms on the top floor of the large, rather dilapidated, semi-detached, Victorian house they shared with their nosey landlady, Mrs Trenchard. She was constantly gossiping about them to the neighbours. She occupied all the rooms downstairs. It must have been very claustrophobic confined to a couple of rooms on the top floor in someone else's house.

They had to share their landlady's kitchen, scullery and outside toilet because like most married couples back then, they couldn't afford a place of their own. In fact, nearly half the population back in the first half of the Fifties were not home owners and had to resort to renting a place in which to live from a private landlord or landlady. The trend of renting from the private sector had continued since the Victorian Age.

There was an acute shortage of housing both before the First and Second World War, and after. The young couple living with their landlady were therefore not alone in their predicament. Demobilisation and the subsequent increase in the birth rate, during the post war era put further strain on the need to increase the supply of housing.

Lloyd George's election promise in 1918 to provide "Homes fit for Heroes" for soldiers returning home from serving in the First World War, started with the Housing and Town Planning Act 1919. (It is also referred to as the Addison Act, named after its author the Minister for Health Dr. Christopher Addison. He had written about the relationship between poor housing and health, namely the filthy and overcrowded slums and how these contributed to poor health; his book '*Betrayal of the Slums*' was published in 1922). This Act made it the responsibility of local authorities (councils) to provide new council owned housing for working class people.

There were several Housing Acts during the interwar period. The Housing Act 1930, (also known as the Greenwood Housing Act of 1930) required councils to clear all of the remaining slums and rehouse those effected. Although, many slums had been demolished and people rehoused in newly constructed homes under this Act, clearing the slums and overcrowding was still a problem that had to be put on hold due to the Second World War.

The need for housing was so acute after the Second World War that thousands of desperate people without a home, mostly ex-service men and their families, became squatters; they occupied disused military service camps dotted all over the country, during August, 1946. The following month the 'squatter movement' consisting of over a thousand people set up camp in abandoned luxury houses and flats, most notably in expensive areas of London: Kensington, Pimlico and St John's Wood.

Properties were either dilapidated due to age and neglect or bomb damaged or destroyed by the enemy's aerial assault during the wartime Blitz. The V-1's (the world's first cruise missile), labelled as 'buzz bombs' and 'doodlebugs', and the V-2 rockets (the world's first long-range ballistic missile) were responsible for a lot of the destruction.

Both political parties had pledged to pull down the slums and in their place build new homes. However, the post-war Labour Government found themselves beset by a series of balance of payments crises, which interrupted the rebuilding programme. The government also viewed overseas commitments as more of a priority and so put their housing policy on the backburner.

During the war the defence budget was an obvious priority and this continued after the war with the defence budget increased to deal with the outbreak of the Korean War, which started on 25th June, 1950. Besides, Britain was heavily in debt after the war, so unfortunately for our young couple, funding new housing was a slow process.

I expected that like most young couples, the young couple in our street would move out of their lodgings and set up home together when more homes were made available and when they had saved up enough to put down a deposit on their own place. Or if they were lucky enough, they may be offered one of the many thousands of council houses, which both the Labour Government and the incoming Conservative Government in October, 1951, had pledged and started to build in earnest.

A temporary solution to the post-war housing crisis was provided for by the Housing (Temporary Accommodation) Act

1944. Under the Emergency Factory Made housing plan (EFM), prefabricated homes were manufactured quickly and cheaply in the factory and assembled on site. These temporary, single storey, two bedroom, detached bungalows known as 'prefabs' could be assembled in a matter of hours! Prefab's were also small, which is why they were often referred to as 'rabbit hutches', a term coined by the then Minister of Health Aneurin Bevan who was also responsible for housing at the time. His priority was to provide accommodation of good quality rather than churning out greater numbers of inadequate dwellings.

In spite of their compact size these temporary homes were of good quality. Everything that a resident might need was provided. These dwellings were even decorated, with magnolia paint on the walls, and contrasting green paint on skirting boards and door surrounds. They featured all the latest mod cons: a fitted kitchen with a built in oven; fitted cupboards and shelves, a gas fridge and a water heater. The bathroom had a fitted bath and there was also a separate flushing toilet. As well as having an open fire there was also a back boiler, which provided not only constant hot running water but also a rudimentary form of central heating. These properties also came with a garden at the front and to the rear.

Unfortunately, for our young couple, returning service personnel of the armed forces and their families were given priority for one of these prefabricated homes. These temporary prefabs were only supposed to last for approximately ten years. However, many occupants were so happy in their new prefab homes that they refused to leave, after the time frame had expired for this temporary type of dwelling. Many residents remained in their prefabs decades later.

Many more homes were still required so local authorities took the initiative and built permanent, pre-cast reinforced concrete houses (PRC), made from concrete panels manufactured in the factory and reinforced and bolted together with steel. These properties were also quick to assemble on site and once again also relied on cheap, unskilled labour. These three-bedroomed council owned properties also provided mod cons. They included a new, fitted kitchen; a bathroom; an inside toilet; a water heater supplying hot running water on tap; heat and light was provided at the flick of a switch. These properties also came with a front and back garden.

Obtaining a council house, however, was not easy; allocation of a local authority dwelling was determined on a points system. The criteria used were based on factors, such as the applicants' ability to pay the council rent, which would have gone in our young couple's favour; they both had, I suspect, reasonably well paid and secure jobs. Council houses were also allocated on a priority basis. Priority was given to those applicants who were in work that was considered offering essential services. Possibly her being a nurse would be a point in her favour, but her husband's job as an office worker, would not.

Priority would also be given to those in greatest need, which included the applicants' current housing situation, and the number of children per household. The fact that our young couple were living in relatively tolerable accommodation, and did not, as yet, have any dependents would not have gone in their favour. But our young couple were not the sort to make themselves purposely homeless or to have children, merely so that they could improve their position on the waiting list for a council house.

Besides, council housing was geared towards blue-collar workers, that is, manual workers, on a low income who could not afford to pay private rent. (Daphne, being a nurse was a pink-collar (female) worker, while her husband who worked in an office was a white-collar worker.) Our young couple appeared to be in a position where they could afford to pay as private tenants since they were living in a private dwelling paying their landlady rent. So for now, it seemed that they had no other option but to share a house with a virtual stranger. Though the tide was changing with the Housing Act 1949, which enabled local authorities to build housing for the population in general, that is for white collar workers, as well as for manual workers on a low income.

In the interim, I wondered why the young couple didn't live with either one of their parents. It was common practice for most newly married couples to live with one set of parents, usually the bride's, parents, since they couldn't afford a place of their own. Or it's possible that neither sets of parents had sufficient room to house them both; if this was the case, a married couple would often be forced to live apart. Perhaps that's why they chose to live together as part of someone else's household, temporarily, until they could find a place to accommodate just themselves.

Perhaps our young couple didn't come from around this area but moved into our street to be nearer to their workplace. Or perhaps they didn't want to start their married life off together living under the watchful eye of their parents, preferring instead to fly the nest in a bid for a bit more independence.

* * *

Our young couple looked like such a romantic couple; they behaved as if they were still on their honeymoon. They only appeared to have eyes for each other; I would often catch them gazing adoringly into each other's eyes. It was only to be expected since they had recently married and so must have been very much in love. I overheard cruel gossips say: "wait until the novelty of married life wears off!"

Their married name was Mr and Mrs Westcott, but they were friendly enough to not mind those in the neighbourhood calling them by their Christian names. The young lady's name was Daphne and her husband's name was Dennis. They must have been in their early to mid-twenties. This was the average age of the majority of couples getting married back then. Most young ladies in the early Fifties were married off by the time they reached the age of twenty-one.

Daphne was slim, petite and pretty, with short, fair hair in the wavy style with a short fringe that was very fashionable in the early Fifties. Her short fringe reminded me of the American film star and singer, Doris Day, in the pictures I had seen of her in film magazines, such as 'Picturergoer'. Daphne had blue-green eyes. Dennis was taller and slim with light blue eyes and light brown hair.

Daphne dressed in the clothes that were fashionable in the first half of the Fifties. I would see her wearing the slim, calf-length pencil skirts, and the fuller skirts and dresses worn with several starched petticoats underneath to accentuate their fullness. Tucked into her skirts she would wear a blouse or shirt with a pretty Peter Pan collar and short cap sleeves.

She would sometimes accessorise her outfit by wearing a short scarf (kerchief) tied around her neck, and a wide, tight-fitting belt that accentuated her small waist. She would often wear with her skirts a tight-fitting jumper or cardigan with feminine looking sleeves that reached just past the elbow. She would complete the look by wearing the ubiquitous stiletto heels.

I liked them both. Daphne was friendly and always seemed to have a smile on her face. She was quietly spoken. She was also shy like me and seemed to be a very fair-minded person, caring, considerate and polite; I liked to think I too, possessed those qualities she had. Mrs Trenchard tried to take advantage of her kind and gentle nature. She knew Daphne wouldn't say no to her demands; she was far too polite for that.

Daphne's husband Dennis, was also reserved like his wife but appeared to be the stronger character of the two, able to speak his mind when he had to. He also reminded me of myself, or how I would have liked to be.

I presumed that Dennis must have served his eighteen months in the national service, which was compulsory peace-time conscription for all fit and able young men between the ages of seventeen and twenty-one. During the Second World War, under the National Service (Armed Forces) Act 1939, the age-range was broader, from eighteen to forty-one, which included the compulsory undertaking of six months military training. (The age limit rose again with a second Act in December 1941. The Act also now included the conscription of unmarried women between the ages of twenty to thirty, due to the severe labour shortage caused by men being called up; later, married women were also conscripted).

The Labour Government introduced the National Service Amendment Act 1948, which now required serving for eighteen months (this superseded the National Service Act 1947, which only provided for one year's service) to provide the country with a reserve of trained, armed forces should war ever break out again. A reserve of troops was also required to help the regular men and women serving in the armed forces to oversee Britain's increasing defence commitments overseas during the post-war era: in Europe, the Middle East, and Asia, and in Africa.

Britain had declared states of emergencies in the British colonies of Malaya and Kenya; Malaya in 1948, which was still ongoing, and in Kenya in 1952. Troops were required in these hotspots to curb civil unrest and maintain order. There were also troubles festering in Egypt over control of the strategically important Suez Canal. Thousands of conscripts were sent there in the first half of the Fifties to deal with the civil unrest. Most young men received their call-up papers on or around the time of their eighteenth birthday.

The few exceptions who were able to defer, were those young men enrolled on a course of study or who were doing work considered of national importance, specifically, farming, coal mining and those employed in the merchant navy. According to this criterion, I don't think Dennis' job working in an office in our local high street in town would have qualified as a job of national importance. Unless of course, he was handling sensitive documents of national importance, but I'm pretty sure this wasn't the case.

The length of time young men had to serve increased from eighteen months to two years in September, 1950, due to the Korean War; Britain became involved as part of the United Nations armed forces in June, 1950. The Labour Government first sent British troops at the end of August, 1950, to aid the American-led United Nations forces. Conscripts were also placed on a reserve list for four years, which was lowered by six months when the length of service was increased to two years. I expect that Dennis was probably on the reserve list, so he could have been called up again at any time, which must have been an unsettling thought for this pair of newly-weds.

I sometimes saw Dennis set off for work in the morning, if I was up early enough to observe him from my bedroom window; I also sometimes saw him return home at night. He cycled to work, which is what most people did back in those days, or took the bus or train. These were the main modes of transport due to the absence of cars, which were mainly to help the export drive after the war since Britain was financially broke. There was also a lack of raw materials for car production; these were prioritised for military defence. Besides, cars were far too expensive for the average person to purchase. Due to the factors mentioned above there was also a waiting list; potential buyers would have to wait for up to two years before being able to acquire a car.

Dennis always carried a brown briefcase in the front basket of his bike. He dressed very smartly in his single-breasted, dark grey flannel suit with a handkerchief protruding from the breast pocket.

He teamed his suit with a plain white shirt and slim, plain, dark-coloured tie. He wore dark brown, polished shoes. A trilby hat completed the look. Men of all ages wore a hat in the respectable, conformist first half of the fifties. Dennis often wore a scarf round his neck, if it was cold, which it invariably was back then. It looked like an old college scarf, with distinctive bottle green, black and gold stripes.

When Dennis wasn't working he wore causal clothes. These consisted of brown flannel trousers, a check shirt, and or a multi-coloured knitted jumper, a mid-brown corduroy jacket and brown coloured loafers.

I happened to overhear Mrs Trenchard discussing her lodger's line of work with a neighbour once: "He works in an office. I'm not sure what he does; he's a technician or something like that with a fancy name!" Actually, he was a draughtsman. He must have been good at technical drawing. He didn't have far to cycle, as he worked in an office above a shop in the high street in our town centre.

I recall overhearing Daphne saying that she was glad that her husband didn't have to commute to London. I recall, this was in winter when dense fog or 'pea-soupers', as these were generally known, descended on London and shrouded the capital in a thick, dirty yellowish-brown, noxious smelling cloud. People resulted to wearing face masks to protect themselves from inhaling this noxious substance. The fog was so bad that it almost completely obscured visibility; tragically it caused many fatalities on the roads and in the River Thames because people couldn't see where they were walking.

This was the sort of fog that intensified with smoke discharged from chimneys, referred to universally as, 'smog'. Smog is a portmanteau of the words smoke and fog. It was this pollutant in the atmosphere that when mixed with cold fog in a heavily built-up area, caused the smog.

Smoke from coal fire emissions were a common sight in big, densely populated industrial cities, such as London. This is where London derived its nickname 'The Smoke'. Heavy smoke occurred in industrial cities from the start of the Industrial Revolution, through the Victorian age, to the second half of the twentieth century, the Fifties. Coal powered the numerous factories in cities, such as London, as well as domestic fires. Everyone had coal fires in those days before modern electric and gas central heating.

The 'Great Smog' hit the capital from 5th to 9th December, 1952; it was the worst smog outbreak that claimed many lives. Thousands, mainly the vulnerable, young, old and sick, succumbed to the smog and died of respiratory diseases, such as, bronchitis and pneumonia.

The Great Smog of London tragedy led the Conservative Government to introduce the first Clean Air Act 1956. This new Act tackled the problem by creating smokeless zones in the heavily congested capital of London and other major cities; in these areas only smokeless fuels could be burned. As a nurse, Daphne understood more than most, the health hazards of this noxious substance, called smog.

I saw Daphne more often than her husband; she worked shifts, as a nurse at the local hospital. They both appeared to be cheerful in spite of their living arrangements, which were far from ideal. I suppose they were happy enough in each other's company to not let a little thing, such as an interfering busybody of a landlady, trouble them. That was, until they could afford to move out and get a place of their own. I expect their marriage had cemented their relationship creating a strong bond to enable them to weather any storm, such as the one posed by their present living conditions.

It's such a pity though, that they had to start off their married life by living with a landlady, and a nosey, gossiping landlady at that! She was the archetypical landlady, both strict and stern. She seemed intent on spoiling their idyllic dream of a married life together, as she tried to create a wedge between the young married couple, for her own selfish reasons. She was constantly medalling in their affairs.

* * *

Old Mrs Trenchard was a widow. She must have been in her sixties or seventies, at least. She was rotund and leaned heavily on her walking stick that she used because of a slight limp, which, according to a rumour I had heard, was caused by polio. Mrs Trenchard's limp confined her mostly indoors; this probably resulted in her pallid complexion.

135

Polio (poliomyelitis) was rife in the Fifties. But a medical breakthrough was achieved during this decade; however, it was too late for Mrs Trenchard to benefit from it.

An American medical research scientist and virologist named Jonas Salk, developed a killed-virus vaccine for polio, delivered by injection, in 1952. A mass clinical trial was undertaken in 1954 before the vaccine's safety and effectiveness was declared to the world in 1955. Another American, Albert Sabin, also a medical research scientist and virologist, worked on the polio oral, live-virus vaccine, carrying out limited trials between 1954 and 1961, at the end of which the vaccine became commercially available.

In common with most people of mature years, Mrs Trenchard wore spectacles, small, brass-rimmed spectacles. She probably couldn't be bothered to replace hers with a new pair provided by the National Health Service (NHS). Apparently, there was a very long waiting period for NHS glasses, and so by the time the recipient got a new pair their prescription had often changed. The glasses that were no longer fit for purpose ended up being discarded in a drawer collecting dust!

Also, in common with a lot of people back in those days, Mrs Trenchard had several teeth missing. A large proportion of the population had lost several, if not all of their teeth prior to the inception of the National Health Service, which came into effect on 5th July, 1948. They just couldn't afford to pay to go to the dentist each time they had a problem with their teeth.

Having to pay to see a dentist sometimes prompted young newly-weds, or at least brides-to-be who had been scrimping and saving to get married, to take the drastic measure of having all of their teeth removed! Rather this, than face the dreaded dentists' drill each time they had a problem with their teeth and the bill at the end! Instead, they preferred to have a new set of dentures that would ensure they would no longer have to pay a costly visit to the dentist ever again.

After the introduction of the National Health Service, some people were still afraid to go to the dentist, and I suspect that Mrs Trenchard was one of those. After all, people like Mrs Trenchard had managed to go without a visit to the dentist for all those years so why bother now, which was probably her way of thinking.

Besides, in 1951, the Labour Government imposed for the first time, charges on National Health Service spectacles and dentures. This political move by the Labour Government must have strengthened Mrs Trenchard's resolve not to visit the dentist, or the optician; like her teeth, she would hang on to her old pair of spectacles too.

The Labour Government's Chancellor of the Exchequer, Hugh Gaitskell, had to make savings in his 1951 Budget to pay for the increased expenditure on defence, with a dramatic increase in rearmament due to the Korean War. The unexpected and exorbitant cost of running the National Health Service, which was draining money, caused this area of the social services to become the obvious target to make savings.

However, these new NHS charges caused several Labour Ministers to resign. The Minister of Labour, Aneurin (Nye) Bevan resigned in disgust. He was previously the Minister of Health and the chief architect of the NHS who had the responsibility on his able shoulders of pushing through the National Health Service bill, which was beset with difficulties. President of the Board of Trade, Harold Wilson, together with Junior Minister at the Ministry of Supply, John Freeman, also resigned. They all resigned at what they perceived as an act against the very principle of a National Health Service that was supposedly free to everyone. Especially since the imposition of these charges were to pay for an unrealistic rearmament programme.

Mrs Trenchard paid more attention to her hair than her teeth. Like many women of mature years, she always had her wavy, grey hair piled on top of her head, styled in the Forties fashionable poodle cut; the curls stayed on top aided by dozens of clips. Her hair couldn't have been naturally wavy because I had sometimes seen her with pins or clips in her hair to keep her pin curls in place, or I had spotted her at the hairdressers where she was able to have her usual weekly shampoo and set. Hairdressers did a booming business after the war, due in no small part to the trend for waves and curls.

I could never understand why Mrs Trenchard went to all that trouble with her hair, when in common with a lot of housewives she often covered her carefully coiffured hair with a scarf tied into a turban. She had probably got into the habit of wearing a turban during the war; many women wore one in that era. The turban was a multifunctional form of headwear. It protected their hair, especially when working with potentially dangerous machinery in the factories and on the farms. Also when women were unable to wash their hair frequently, with water on ration and shampoo in short supply, as was soap, they could hide their unwashed hair under a turban.

All soaps came off ration as late as September 1950, so the turban still had its uses after the war. A turban was also useful to protect the hair from dirt and grime when doing one's housework. Alternatively, the turban could be used in-between visits to the hairdresser, to hide unmanageable hair.

I would also see Mrs Trenchard wearing with her turban, a pinny (apron or housecoat) over her day clothes, when, due to her slight physical disability, she undertook light cleaning duties. She would wear this apparel when polishing and flicking a duster around, which was often, since this activity didn't require much physical exertion. Besides, undertaking light cleaning duties came in useful when she wanted to eavesdrop on her young lodgers.

I had heard all about Mrs Trenchard prying into the young couple's personal business! She was one of the notorious gossips in our street. As was Mrs Green, she was married to nice Mr Green. (I have, as you will have noted, also included this older, married couple in this first Volume of my character portrayal.) There was also Mrs Starling; she shared her house with her secretive lodger whom I nicknamed our Mystery Man. (He is included in Volume III.) The old gossipmongers, like Mrs Trenchard, seemed to spend their time criticising other neighbours, especially the younger ones who had more modern ideas. "Fanciful ideas", is the phrase they used.

The early Fifties was still an era of staunch conservativism and strict adherence to authority. Although, change was afoot in the coming years of that decade, the older residents in our street stubbornly tried to resist change with their outmoded ideas. They were still living in the past.

Mrs Trenchard always seemed to have plenty to say about her young married lodgers. Just because they lived under *her* roof, she thought it gave her the right to judge them, and talk about them and what they got up to in *her* house. She was two-faced. She could be pleasant to them when she wanted something from them, but she was quite happy to talk about them behind their back and even to their face.

I called her, 'old acid drop' behind her back, of course. She had the sort of face that reminded me of an acid drop: on the exterior, she more often than not, had a sour expression on her aged face and an acid tongue to go with it! But she could be sweet and all smiles when it was in her favour to be.

By all accounts Mrs Trenchard was a harridan! Daphne and Dennis must have felt like being back at school with a strict schoolmistress constantly telling them what they could and couldn't do. She had rules that she expected the young couple to adhere to while they were living under *her* roof. No smoking, no drinking, no pets and no inviting friends over without asking her permission first.

Mrs Trenchard had double standards, according to Daphne. Daphne had found her smoking the odd cigarette and she often liked a drink in the evenings. She also owned a pet cat. And sometimes she would actively encourage Daphne and her husband to invite friends over, presumably so that she could be nosey and ask them personal questions for her own amusement.

* * *

Mrs Trenchard considered her cat before she considered her lodgers or, "house guests", as she liked to call them. She called her cat Humphrey after her favourite film star, Humphrey Bogart. (Her liking for Mr Bogart was something that she shared in common with Mrs Green, who, as I mentioned in the Chapter on Mr and Mrs Green, was also a fan.) Humphrey was a long-haired cat with fur the colour of deep grey. I'm not sure what breed it was, only that it was a pedigree, or so its owner kept boasting.

Mrs Trenchard allowed Humphrey access to the whole house, unlike her house guests who she did not afford that privilege. She even allowed him in the scullery and kitchen, and to jump up onto the kitchen table! Daphne found this objectionable and said it was very unhygienic. There were cat odours and fur flying everywhere, which was why Daphne said she probably wouldn't have been surprised if she, like the cat, had hairballs inside her stomach from inhaling all the cat hairs! Daphne shooed the cat away gently when Mrs Trenchard was not around.

Humphrey would often find his way upstairs and into the young couple's rooms. He had given Daphne a fright on several occasions. The way he was quick and nimble on his paws, artfully darting about and sneaking up on her when she was least expecting it, especially at night! Daphne said the cat had sometimes frightened her when she was all alone in the house. Suddenly she would spy a pair of piercing amber-coloured eyes glowing at her from the dark recesses!

She said she had nearly tripped over the cat on several occasions when it ran past her and scurried down the stairs. Daphne said she was more worried about knocking over one of Mrs Trenchard's precious porcelain vases that she kept on an occasional table on the landing, than falling over and hurting herself! I don't know why Mrs Trenchard had to have all these porcelain ornaments, which served no real purpose, on permanent display in her house with a cat let loose! I suspect it must have been just for show.

According to Daphne, who relayed all these tales to my mother, which I overheard, the cat also had a habit of bringing dead mice inside, much to her horror! It once dropped one at her feet and looked up at her, as if it expected praise! Daphne told my mother she couldn't help but let out a scream.

On another occasion, the cat leapt out from its hiding place in a cubby hole underneath the large butler sink in the scullery. Most homes had a large butler or Belfast sink (the latter originated in Belfast, and had an overflow system) in the kitchen or scullery. A small curtain pulled across the small cubbyhole beneath it, screened the area to hide the snug space housing bits and bobs, such as cleaning materials. The cat gave Daphne such a fright that she dropped the delicate bone china plate she was holding, which crashed to the floor and broke into tiny pieces. She said, fortunately Mrs Trenchard was out that day so she couldn't complain. However, Daphne felt she had to own up to the breakage, as sooner or later Mrs Trenchard would have noticed the missing plate.

On hearing about the incident with the plate Mrs Trenchard tutted and scolded Daphne for being so clumsy. Daphne said she offered to replace the plate with a similar item but Mrs Trenchard informed her in no uncertain terms that the item was "irreplaceable!" Daphne said she could not placate Mrs Trenchard; she made her feel like a naughty schoolgirl!

Daphne said Humphrey the cat, tended to make an appearance in the kitchen when she was about to prepare tea or a late supper; he was always scrounging for food, any titbits or leftovers. Daphne told my mother of an incident involving some fresh fish that she had patiently queued up for and purchased from the fishmongers in town. Fresh fish, was never on ration, not even during the war, probably because it was a perishable foodstuff and it was often difficult to obtain.

The fishing industry had not yet recovered from the Second World War. During the war the blockade prevented supply ships and fishing vessels from entering and exiting ports. Most fishing vessels during the Battle of the Atlantic that were prevented from going out to sea were commandeered or requisitioned for war service. Fishermen were also reluctant to fish in German U-boat (submarine) invested waters, or those who were able-bodied seamen were drafted into helping the Navy with their wartime operations.

After the war, fish was highly sought after since meat was on ration until July, 1954, the last food item to be derationed. As a consequence of this, there were always shortages of fish, as in wartime, and prices fluctuated, as these were not at first regulated.

Also fish stock in unrestricted areas that had not been mined during the war had been over fished, consequently certain fish stock depleted during and just after the war, had not yet recovered. Hence, fish was scarce so there were always long queues outside the fishmongers back in wartime and after the war. Although coastal towns like ours faired a little better when it came to obtaining certain types of fish, namely shellfish.

Daphne explained that she had bought a nice piece of haddock, which she had intended to give to her husband for his tea when he returned from work. But unbeknown to her, Mrs Trenchard, on spying the fish, decided to take it and fed it to her cat! Apparently, Mrs Trenchard made up some cock and bull story that she thought Daphne had bought the fish for her cat Humphrey, as a special treat, knowing full well that during rationing it was forbidden to feed pets' food for human consumption only.

The exception was 'Snoek', a species of snake mackerel (barracouta, scientific name: Thyrsites atun), a suspect sounding, looking and tasting fish. This was shipped over from South Africa during the war as a cheaper, tinned fish alternative to salmon, which cost more on the points system. When rationing was in force, a number of points were allocated to every person; it was a method for distributing non-essential foodstuffs, such as tinned fish.

However, the British consumer didn't take to Snoek's unusual taste; they were also put off by its suspect name. The Ministry of Food even concocted a fancy recipe for 'Snoek Piquant' during the war but couldn't tempt anyone to eat it! (Imported whale meat, also from South Africa, which was apparently very oily and smelly, didn't fare much better with the consumer either.)

Since there were tons of Snoek tins leftover from the war years, these were relabelled and sold off as pet food for cats and kittens. But not for Humphrey, I hasten to add, who apparently also turned his nose up at it in disgust. Daphne said Mrs Trenchard, on being told of the error in feeding her prized piece of haddock to Humphrey, never even attempted to replace it!

Another time, Daphne was about to heat up a little milk that she had left in a saucepan for her and her husband's night time drink of Horlicks, when she noticed that the pan was empty. She then heard a noise on the floor and it was Humphrey the cat lapping up the remains of what must have been their milk, off a saucer, which had been placed on the kitchen floor. She said all she could do was watch helplessly. After finishing off the milk, the cat simply licked its paws with a look of contentment.

* * *

Never mind the cat, Daphne laughingly told my mother, they had to be as quiet as mice around the house trying to avoid Mrs Trenchard because of her nosiness. But it was difficult to avoid her when they were virtually living on top of each other and sharing communal areas, such as the kitchen and scullery. Mrs Trenchard also had ample opportunity to meet them on the landing or in the hallway and ask them all sorts of nosey questions. They felt compelled to tiptoe around, especially when entering and exiting their bedroom and living room, or the kitchen and scullery, in case Mrs Trenchard was on the prowl!

As soon as Mrs Trenchard heard a door creak open or being closed, she would manage to vacate the room she was in with the aid of her walking stick and be on the landing or in the hallway, her eyes on stalks! Dennis suspected that this was probably why she didn't want the creaking doors repaired, when he offered to repair them.

The couple always had to be constantly on their guard. They also had to be careful not to talk too loudly in case Mrs Trenchard worked out which room they were in, or overheard them and their conversation. Daphne joked that an evening course in sign language would have been beneficial. They were only grateful that Mrs Trenchard was a little hard of hearing. She could hear sounds, but she found it more difficult to decipher words, so she was unable to pick up on all their private conversations.

Daphne and her husband tried to use the kitchen when Mrs Trenchard wasn't around, but it wasn't easy. Once she found out their routine she used to time it so that she was using the kitchen at the same time as either of them. She would then observe them at close quarters, especially Daphne, as she went about trying to prepare a meal, and would, "proffer her advice", according to Daphne's husband.

Mrs Trenchard was always observing their movements, such as at what time they both went to work and what time they both returned. I overheard her tell a neighbour: "He's gone for most of the day, starting out early in the morning just after dawn and arriving back home just before dusk! While she works shifts so she's out any time of the day or night!"

Understandably, Daphne said they felt they had no privacy. When Mrs Trenchard didn't see one of them going to work she would be nosey and enquire if one of them was ill. Daphne said Mrs Trenchard once even had the gall on hearing that Daphne had been feeling sick one day, to put two and two together and come to the wrong conclusion about her condition, being a woman of childbearing age. Daphne found this just too intimate, personal and upsetting.

Unfortunately, for Daphne, because she worked shifts she was often around the home more than her husband Dennis. This gave

Mrs Trenchard more opportunity to "collar her", as Daphne called it, and ask her "all manner of questions".

Since Daphne was shy and reserved, she found herself unable to avoid answering often personal questions. She said she felt quite helpless, as she didn't know how to handle Mrs Trenchard for fear of being rude. She found it difficult to cope on her own, unable to defend herself without the protection of her husband who was more capable of standing up to Mrs Trenchard's nosey inquisitiveness. He was more skilled at fencing around personal questions. Daphne said he was able to deal with Mrs Trenchard more tactfully, without giving too much away about themselves.

Daphne also said when she was on her own Mrs Trenchard would often invite her into her living room downstairs in the daytime to sit with her and keep her company. She also wanted Daphne to sit with her and listen to 'Mrs Dale's Diary' on the radio.

This long running serial drama ran from 1948 (to 1969), and was broadcast every weekday afternoon and repeated the morning after. In 'Mrs Dale's Diary', Mrs Dale noted in her diary the goings-on in the suburbs where she resided with her doctor husband Jim. She was forever worrying about her husband, as she was constantly exclaiming, "I'm rather worried about Jim". This phrase she used became a popular catchphrase with the audience. I'm sure this gossip-fuelled drama satisfied Mrs Trenchard's inquisitive nature. Also because it was about a doctor and medical matters, she thought Daphne would be tempted to join her and listen to it. Daphne, of course, was in the medical profession working as a nurse.

Daphne said she often found it difficult to refuse to sit and listen to the radio with Mrs Trenchard despite being busy. Daphne said she preferred to listen to the factual programme aimed specifically at women, 'Women's Hour', if she was home in the afternoons. She would listen to it whilst she undertook chores that needed attending to before she went back to work on shift duty. Daphne said if she was home in the morning, she could often hear Mrs Trenchard listening to the popular morning show, 'Housewives Choice', which played listeners' record requests.

Mrs Trenchard would also invite Daphne in the evenings when Daphne's husband was out or doing overtime at the office where he worked. (Back in the Fifties, people worked long hours.) She wanted Daphne to have a drink with her and listen to the evening broadcast of the new serial on the radio, '*The Archers*', (which now claims credit for being the world's longest running serial drama to date).

Mrs Trenchard was gripped by this more down-to-earth rival to, '*Mrs Dale's Diary*', when it first aired to the nation on 1st, January, 1951. (Pilot episodes had previously been broadcast on the BBC's Midlands Home Service during the Spring Bank Holiday, which began on 29th May, 1950.)

'*The Archers*' was set on a farm and advertised as, "A tale of everyday country folk", according to the programme promoters. It was also meant to be educational, especially for farmers by featuring rural matters. This was important when the population were relying on the land for food due to the rationing of many foodstuffs and limited food imports. Once again, Daphne found it difficult to refuse to sit with Mrs Trenchard and listen to this serial on the radio.

Daphne suspected Mrs Trenchard wanted her to sit with her, especially in the evenings, because she craved companionship. Daphne told my mother that she felt obliged to keep Mrs Trenchard company. But she tried to get out of it when she could, by making up various excuses. She would tell Mrs Trenchard that she had a pile of ironing to do, and had to iron her husband Dennis' shirt for work the next day. But Mrs Trenchard would often refuse to take no for an answer and would retort: "Oh leave that! It can wait until later!"

Daphne said she would then have to sit and listen to Mrs Trenchard going on about the various aliments that afflicted her. Her main gripe was her rheumatism and arthritis, which appeared to afflict every limb and bone in her body. Along with a catalogue of other aches and pains. Old Mrs Trenchard would excuse her drinking her favourite tipple, which was gin, by saying that it was purely for "medicinal purposes."

Daphne said Mrs Trenchard just wanted to unburden herself of her ailments and also wanted a sympathetic ear, and with Daphne, she knew she'd get it! Probably, the fact that Daphne was a nurse was the reason why Mrs Trenchard wanted to unload herself of her aliments, but it was the last thing Daphne said she wanted to do at the end of a tiring shift at work: talk shop!

Daphne told my mother that she would have to sit in Mrs Trenchard's depressingly dark, poorly lit living room. Facing her on the wall were dull, sepia-coloured, framed portraits of Mrs Trenchard's dear, departed relatives. Daphne would then have to endure a couple of boring hours when Mrs Trenchard brought out old family photograph albums, which looked like they hadn't seen the light of day for a while, being tucked away in a drawer collecting dust. It gave Mrs Trenchard the opportunity to reminisce about past memories of her youth.

Why do elderly people always dwell on the past? I expect she, like them, prefer to relive the past because they don't have as many happy memories to look forward to in the future. Being not as young and sprightly as they once were, I expect the invitations and opportunities for going out and enjoying themselves have dwindled with the passing of time. Older peoples' tendency to cling on to the past, probably explains why some, like Mrs Trenchard, are so old-fashioned in their ways.

Daphne said while she sat with Mrs Trenchard she would become aware of how quiet everything was in her room. She was conscious of the old carriage clock on the mantelpiece, which was now in the foreground, ticking the time away. An assortment of ornaments sat symmetrically placed either side of the clock, which necessitated regular attention from Mrs Trenchard's duster. Daphne was also conscious of the rhythmic clicking sound of Mrs Trenchard's knitting needles, when she wasn't suffering from bouts of rheumatism and arthritis, that is.

Knitting was a very popular hobby back then, as it had been throughout both world wars, when everyone, including men and children, were encouraged to knit for the war effort. There were even knitting circles to teach people how to knit! The population knitted items of clothing, especially socks, gloves, mittens, mufflers, scarves, balaclava's (warm headgear worn under helmets) and hats for soldiers serving abroad in often hostile, cold environments. Ladies magazines displayed advertisements encouraging people to 'do your bit and knit'; some of these magazines also featured knitting patterns.

The British yarn company Sirdar, also produced 'war patterns' to make knitted garments specifically for those serving in the armed forces and for those in the Civil Defence Service (formerly the Air Raid Precautions Service (APS) at home. The company also produced specially colour dyed yarns, in the forces uniform colours.

To get back to Daphne's ordeal of spending most of the evening in the company of Mrs Trenchard, after some time had elapsed Daphne would observe Mrs Trenchard as she eventually nodded off. Daphne wanted desperately to leave at that moment but felt prevented from doing so for fear of awakening her. Every time she tried to make her escape Mrs Trenchard would stir, only awakening briefly to concentrate her steely, blue-eyed gaze in Daphne's direction. Daphne felt trapped! She would be forced to wait until her husband Dennis came home, which was her excuse to finally make good her escape.

Mrs Trenchard would even invite the young couple downstairs to spend their evenings with her by enticing them with the prospect of listening to her radiogram. Her large radiogram was grander than their smaller but perfectly adequate, Ekco radio.

(E. K. Cole (Ekco) was a well established and successful electronics company with their factory based in Essex. The company manufactured radios, and by the mid-fifties, television sets. They were the first to use bakelite plastic as a material for their radio cases and cabinets, producing a series of their famous round bakelite radios during the Thirties.) A radiogram, as well as being a radio, which according to Mrs Trenchard had better reception, also had the added facility of playing gramophone records, hence the name.

She invited the young couple to join her and sit and listen to the British Broadcasting Corporation's, (BBC) Light Programme, which provided light entertainment. There were variety shows, popular music, comedy and some lightweight plays, all of which Mrs Trenchard enjoyed. Daphne said her husband couldn't bear to sit there being forced to listen to variety programmes.

Mrs Trenchard liked the very popular, unscripted variety show, 'Have a Go', with its famous Northern entertainer and compere, Wilfred Pickles and his real life wife Mabel. The show was a live evening broadcast and included audience participation; it claims credit for being the first game show to offer prize money. Ordinary people whom the couple met during the making of the show on their travels across Britain would be invited to 'Have a Go' at the quiz in order to win prize money. One of Pickles famous phrases was, "Give 'im the money, Mabel!"

Mrs Trenchard also enjoyed the popular BBC Light Programme, '*Take It From Here*', which was a musical and comedy sketch show, written by the talented writing duo, Frank Muir and Denis Norden. It first aired on the radio in 1948. Later in the series, in 1953, it included a weekly instalment about '*The Glum Family*'. This was recorded in front of a live audience at midday on Sundays and repeated midweek in the evening.

'*The Glum Family*' centred on a long engaged couple, (played by Dick Bentley and Joy Nichols, later played by a young, then unknown actress June Whitfield). The couple never appear to have any time to themselves whilst living under the roof of 'Pa Glum' (played by Jimmy Edwards), who constantly interrupts their courtship.

Despite the show's huge popularity, Dennis didn't like listening to '*The Glum Family*'. It was too much of a reminder of his own situation with him and his new wife Daphne living under the ever watchful eye of their landlady Mrs Trenchard!

Mrs Trenchard also liked to invite the pair in to her room on a Sunday afternoon to listen to the popular variety show '*The Billy Cotton Band Show*'. Daphne and Dennis were fed up though, with hearing the band leader Billy Cotton's raucous introduction to the show of "Wakey-Wakey!" He placed vocal emphasis on these slang words, meaning, 'wake-up'; this was followed by the introductory music. Dennis said the show was more suited to middle-aged and elderly listeners, who would appreciate light entertainment.

I heard Dennis preferred the comedy, '*Much-Binding-In-The-Marsh*'. Initially about a fictional RAF station and the excessive bureaucracy placed on the senior staff; it starred Richard Murdoch and Kenneth Horne who were also the show's writers. It began on the radio in 1944 and ended its run in 1954. Dennis also liked, '*Ray's a Laugh*', starring the comedian Ted Ray.

I also heard later, as I think they had moved out of their lodgings by then, that Dennis enjoyed the more character based situation comedy (sitcom), '*Hancock's Half-Hour*', which was considered to be the first of its kind on radio. Written by the talented writing duo, Alan Simpson and Ray Galton, it starred the comedian, Tony Hancock, as the main character, with the comedy actor Sidney James, playing his side-kick. The series aired on the radio in 1954 and ran until 1959. (Due to its popularity the show was also shown concurrently on television from 1956, until 1961.)

Dennis was also a fan of the madcap, surreal comedy radio show, '*The Goons*'; it was anarchic in tone and first aired on the radio in May, 1951. It was originally entitled '*Crazy People*'. The stars of the show were comedians, Spike Milligan who was the main contributor to the script writing, Michael Bentine, Peter Sellers and Harry Secombe. The show had a cult following. Dennis enjoyed this sort of unconventional humour because it was innovative.

He and Daphne preferred the BBC's Home Service, which was the main channel for providing national and regional news; it also provided features, talks and drama. The BBC's Third Programme was the remaining channel they enjoyed listening to.

The Third Programme aired in the evening from 6pm and was the highbrow channel with its serious content and high cultural tone. It broadcast news and presented discussion programmes on serious subjects, such as political and current affairs, science and philosophy.

The annual, '*Reith lectures*', were delivered by notables of the day, leaders in their field of expertise. The philosopher, Bertrand Russell, was the first to deliver his series of lectures on philosophy in 1948, when the programme began. (He won the Nobel Prize for literature in 1950. He was also the President of the Campaign for Nuclear Disarmament (CND); he along with Canon John Collins founded this organisation in 1958.)

Scientists invited to participate in the '*Reith lectures*' included the American theoretical physicist, J. Robert Oppenheimer who delivered a series of lectures on this topic in 1953. (At the start of World War Two he directed a team in America who developed the atomic bomb. After the war he opposed the development of the more powerful hydrogen bomb; he lobbied unsuccessfully for international control of nuclear energy between the US and USSR governments.)

The Third Programme also offered its listeners classical music, including contemporary jazz, which appealed to Dennis. The channel's literature content consisted of serious drama, plays and poetry; it was particularly renowned for its portrayal of classical drama and avant-garde plays.

One such play, by the Welsh poet Dylan Thomas, was the critically acclaimed, '*Under Milk Wood*'. It was broadcast on the Third Programme on 25th January, 1954, (after the death of the poet on 9th November, the previous year). It starred amongst the all Welsh cast the Welsh actor, Richard Burton, giving a powerful performance reading the verse with his deep, resonant voice.

Since Dennis was also a huge fan of jazz he also listened to the BBC's late evening, Light Programme, '*Let's Settle For Music*', when it first aired in April, 1952; it was regarded as being the first regular jazz programme. It featured Dennis' favourite trumpeter, Kenny Baker, and his jazz band *Kenny Baker's Dozen*. Previously, Kenny Baker was the lead trumpeter in the British post-war popular jazz band, '*The Ted Heath Band*', which Dennis also enjoyed listening to.

Dennis could play the trumpet. He had learnt to play this instrument when he was in the Boys' Brigade, and presumably later on he was able to brush up on his trumpeting skills when doing his national service. According to what I had also overheard, he kept the trumpet he owned well hidden at the back of the couple's bedroom wardrobe, well away from Mrs Trenchard's clutches! He suspected that she wouldn't approve. He daren't risk playing it when she was out because he didn't want any neighbours overhearing him playing and telling her of his musical activities; he only practiced with some friends elsewhere.

Daphne said Dennis also enjoyed listening to, when he was able to, the trumpeter, Humphrey Lyttelton, and American trumpeters: Louis Armstrong, Dizzy Gillespie, Harry James and Miles Davis. He was also a fan of the female American jazz singers: Ella Fitzgerald, Lena Horne, Sarah Vaughan and Peggy Lee. He was also an admirer of the rising star Cleo Laine, a talented British jazz singer. She performed with the Johnny Dankworth Seven; Johnny Dankworth's big band, the Johnny Dankworth Orchestra, superseded the former band, after 1953. (The couple later married in 1958.)

Mrs Trenchard played a musical instrument. Sometimes she would start playing her old, upright piano, housed in the corner of her sitting room. Most homes had an upright piano prior to the radio (wireless), which superseded the decline of sheet music. Dennis and Daphne would have to listen to Mrs Trenchard tinkling the ivories, playing her favourite, old tunes. Or she would get them to listen on her well used radiogram to her old gramophone records of golden oldies and classic melodies, such as Ivor Novello's *'We'll Gather Lilacs in the Spring'*.

When she wasn't playing her piano or listening to her radiogram, she also enjoyed a game of cards and would often wile away the hours playing a solo game of Patience. When she became bored with playing alone and desired company, she would invite Daphne and Dennis to her room to play a card game of either rummy or gin rummy or a game of Beetle Drive.

Beetle Drive was a very popular game with adults in the Fifties, which required more than one player. (Body parts are either drawn on paper or using die-cuts, which linked together, form the whole beetle; each body part is attached and determined on the roll of a dice.) Daphne said her husband would decline at every opportunity to join her in a parlour game, but occasionally he would give in just to keep the peace with Mrs Trenchard.

Daphne thought Mrs Trenchard was lonely, but Daphne's husband could see right through her! It was just a ruse. Her real motive for inviting them into her room was so that she could question them about their comings and goings to satisfy her curiosity and nosiness. Or perhaps she didn't want to hear their radio interfering with her radiogram or her piano-playing. Or it was to save on electricity and heat by them all being confined to one room. Daphne said her husband complained: "Why would we want to spend our evenings of the first year of our married life with her!" They didn't want her constantly in the background ogling them! Besides, she had her own family, if she chose to get along with family members, such as her son-in-law, and she had her cat!

Due to Mrs Trenchard's nosiness, Daphne and Dennis felt they couldn't invite friends over because she would ask too many questions, a point I made earlier. The following day Daphne said Mrs Trenchard would want, "a post-mortem of their activities and conversations." She would interrogate Daphne: "Who are they?" "How did you meet them?" "What do they do?" "Where do they live?" Daphne innocently thought it was probably just Mrs Trenchard's way of showing an interest, but her husband Dennis

151

perceptively saw through this pretence, that she was being nosey as usual.

Mrs Trenchard would also keep finding excuses to interrupt the young couple, which happened on the very few occasions when they did invite a couple of friends over at the weekend. She kept making an excuse to knock on their door in order that she could observe what was going on. She asked Daphne and Dennis if they had borrowed a newspaper of hers, or did she leave her knitting in their room when she had visited earlier in the day? On clapping her eyes on their guests, Daphne said she would exclaim: "Well, aren't you going to introduce me to your friends?"

* * *

I knew both Daphne and Dennis were keen ballroom dancers and so would much prefer to spend their evenings out attending the local dance hall, rather than staying in entertaining Mrs Trenchard. The ballroom is where I heard they first met. Ballroom dancing was an extremely popular leisure activity during the Fifties, second only to the cinema. Apparently, Dennis had won several medals for ballroom dancing, for waltzes and the faster paced foxtrot.

The couple were also both keen filmgoers. Britain was a nation of cinemagoers in the Fifties before the introduction of television into peoples' homes. This coincided with the televised Coronation of Queen Elizabeth the Second, in June, 1953.

Many people got their first television set in time for the Coronation so that they could watch this spectacular event in the comfort of their own home. Or failing that, they got a television after they had watched the event on someone else's set, or at the local church hall, pub or cinema. It has been estimated that over half the population in Britain watched the Coronation on television. However, over half of these watched it on someone else's television or participated in a mass viewing at public places, such as pubs, dance and church halls, and of course, at cinemas.

Being interested in dancing, Daphne was also a fan of the Hollywood musicals made in Technicolor. Daphne was spoilt for choice when it came to watching musicals, as there were many produced in the first half of the Fifties.

She told me she saw the Hollywood musical, '*An American in Paris*', when it was shown in our local cinema in 1951. It starred American actor Gene Kelly, and the French actress and dancer Leslie Caron. The film won an American Academy Award for Best Picture. Daphne also saw, '*Lillie*', released in 1953, again starring Leslie Caron. She also went to see, '*Singin' in the Rain*', released in 1952, once again starring the versatile dancer, choreographer, actor and co-director of this film, Gene Kelly.

I had also gone to see these two films starring Gene Kelly, and had decided that I wanted to be a dancer, as well as an actress when I grew up. (A little later I decided to become a famous writer.) Daphne, like me, was very impressed with Gene Kelly's spectacular choreography and incredibly well-timed dance routines.

Daphne was also in awe of the fabulous dancing duo, Fred Astaire and Cyd Charisse, as I was; particularly their '*Dancing in the Dark*' dance routine, as seen in the Hollywood romantic musical comedy, '*The Band Wagon*', produced in 1953. Another dancer Daphne and I admired was Ann Miller, especially her tap dancing routine '*Too Darn Hot*', which she performed in the Hollywood romantic musical comedy '*Kiss Me Kate*', also produced in 1953.

Like me, Daphne was a fan of Doris Day and saw her star in several Hollywood musicals during that era: '*On Moonlight Bay*', in 1951, and its sequel, '*By the Light of the Silvery Moon*', in 1953. Both films co-starred Gordon Macrae. The legendary Ms. Day also starred in the successful swashbuckling Wild West film, '*Calamity Jane*', in 1953.

'*Annie Get Your Gun*' was another Hollywood musical set in the Wild West, starring Betty Hutton and Howard Keel. Daphne probably saw it after its release in 1950. She must have seen the famous tenor opera singer, Mario Lanza, starring in the Hollywood musical drama, '*The Great Caruso*', after its release in 1951; it was apparently the most popular film at the British Box Office in 1951.

Then in 1954, there was the musical comedy, '*White Christmas*', starring Bing Crosby, Danny Kaye, Rosemary Clooney and Vera-Ellen. Daphne must have seen, '*Seven Brides for Seven Brothers*', also released in 1954, starring among the large cast, the singer and actor Howard Keel and actress Jane Powell. '*A Star is

Born' was yet another musical released in 1954, starring Judy Garland and James Mason.

Technically minded Dennis was more impressed with the British film, '*The Sound Barrier*', released for public viewing in 1952. It was about attempts by aircraft designers and test pilots to break the sound barrier. It starred Ralph Richardson, Nigel Patrick and Ann Todd, and was a box office success.

I also heard Dennis was fond of comedies. He must have seen at the cinema the hugely successful Ealing Comedies made at the London based Ealing studios.

There was the popular film, '*Whisky Galore*', released in 1949; among its stars were Basil Radford, Bruce Seeton, Joan Greenwood, Gordon Jackson and Gabrielle Blunt. The film was based on a true story about a ship containing a large cargo of whisky that had run aground near the coast of the Outer Hebrides, Scotland and sank due to bad weather during World War Two. In the film the islanders had run out of whisky during the shortages of the Second World War, and on learning of a shipwreck that contained thousands of cases of whisky, decide to help themselves by salvaging the cargo of whisky before the ship sinks. That is, before the local customs and exercise men come to confiscate the whisky!

Another Ealing film, also released in 1949, was the black comedy '*Kind Hearts and Coronets*'. It starred Dennis Price, Valerie Hobson, Joan Greenwood and Alec Guinness. It's about a poor, distant and revengeful relative (Dennis Price) who plots to get rid of other relatives (all played by Alec Guinness) so that he can become heir to the family's aristocratic title and fortune.

'*Passport to Pimlico*' was yet another Ealing film released in 1949. The film centres on Pimlico, a district of London, where one of Pimlico's resident's discovers an old treaty that proves Pimlico is part of Burgundy in France; they declare their independence from Britain as a foreign territory, hence the need for a passport. It starred my favourite actress, Margaret Rutherford; it also starred Stanley Holloway, among the large cast list.

Stanley Holloway also starred alongside Alec Guinness who was Oscar nominated for his performance in the 1951 Ealing comedy '*The Lavender Hill Mob*'. In a plot with his new fellow lodger played by Holloway he steals, with the help of two petty criminals, played by Sidney James and Alfie Bass, gold bullion from the bank where he works as a clerk. The two lodgers hatch a successful plan to smuggle the gold abroad. The film won an Academy award for Best Original Screenplay.

Alec Guinness also starred in another Ealing comedy about lodgers planning a bank robbery. His elderly landlady, played by Katie Johnson, discovers their plan, hence the title: '*The Ladykillers*'. The film was released in December, 1955.

Alec Guinness also starred in the Oscar nominated, '*The Man in the White Suit*', released in 1951; his co-stars were Joan Greenwood and Cecil Parker. Guinness plays a research scientist who, while working as a labourer at a textile mill, invents a suit that never soils; since his invention would put his bosses in the textile industry out of business they attempt to suppress his invention.

Another Ealing comedy, '*The Titfield Thunderbolt*', released in 1953, starred John Gregson and once again, Stanley Holloway. It concerns the attempts by a group of volunteers to keep their village branch train line working after its imminent closure by British Railways. I have outlined summaries of these Ealing Comedies because these films are now considered film classics.

I heard Daphne and Dennis enjoyed going to see the 1953 British-made comedy film, '*Doctor in the House*', which is set in a hospital. It was the first in the Doctor series, adapted from the books written by Richard Gordon. It starred young trainee doctors: Dirk Bogarde, Kenneth More, Donald Sinden and Donald Houston. The love interests were played by the pretty Muriel Pavlow and Kay Kendall. James Robinson-Justice starred as the formidable Surgeon.

I also heard via Daphne that both she and Dennis also enjoyed watching the British box office success, '*Genevieve*', when it went on general release in 1953. I thought this film would appeal to Dennis since it was about the London to Brighton vintage car rally. (I know other neighbours of ours, young Richard and his father, went to see this film: they were mad on cars! I have also included a character study of Richard in Volume II.)

The film '*Genevieve*' starred John Gregson, Dinah Sheridan, Kenneth Moore and Kay Kendall. I think Dennis also enjoyed this film because it had some jazz trumpet playing in it. The legendary Kenny Baker, dubbed Kay Kendall's memorable trumpet playing in the film. Apparently, Daphne and Dennis went to see this film with friends, another married couple.

I realize I've harped on about films, but we were a film-obsessed nation back in the post-war period, before the popularisation of television. After all, going to the pictures was the number one leisure activity in Britain, a point I made previously, (dancing was second).

Cinema attendances reached their peak in 1946, and were still pulling in the crowds, in the first half of the Fifties. However, the lure of television around the time of the televised Queen's Coronation in June, 1953, began to compete with the cinema for its audience.

In order to maintain cinema attendances, the film industry introduced new technical innovations, such as widescreens. Vista Vision was a widescreen format. Prior to Vista Vision in 1954, was the less successful Cinerama in 1952, which introduced its widescreen format.

CinemaScope introduced its widescreen in 1953, shown to excellent effect in the 1953 films, 'How to Marry a Millionaire', and 'The Robe'. Both films claimed credit for being the first to use CinemaScope. 'How to Marry a Millionaire' was the first film photographed in the new Cinemascope; however, the American film production company, Twentieth Century Fox, decided to release its second film, 'The Robe', first. They based their decision to promote CinemaScope first on 'The Robe' because of the film's epic scale; they rightly believed the new widescreen technology used for this particular film would enthral audiences.

The film industry also employed gimmicks, such as special effects 3-D (three dimensional) images. Audiences wore stereoscopic, polarised 3-D goggles to view such films as the American, 1952 tropical adventure 'Bwana Devil', which started a craze in 3-D films. (The cheaper, disposable cardboard 3-D glasses were used to view films shown at the Festival of Britain in 1951.)

'Bwana Devil' premiered in Britain, in London and other major cities, in March, 1953; the film's claim to fame was for being the first colour stereoscopic film. The 1953, 3-D horror film, 'House of Wax', was also not on general release here in Britain. Its claim to fame was being the first 3-D film to feature stereophonic sound.

156

There were also the epic films, which were lavish, expensive productions produced on a huge budget, employing an unprecedented cast of extras. These ranged from tropical adventures on location, such as, the 1950 Hollywood film, '*King Solomon's Mines*', starring Deborah Kerr, Stewart Granger and Richard Carlson, to extravagant biblical epics.

Hollywood's, first film in the popular biblical genre, was the 1949 film '*Samson and Delilah*'; its principal stars were Victor Mature and Hedy Lamarr. It was the highest grossing film in the United States and the second most popular film watched by British cinemagoers after its release here in 1950. This film established the biblical epic.

Films in the same biblical genre that followed were: '*David and Bathsheba*' starring Gregory Peck and Susan Hayward, and '*Quo Vadis*', with Robert Taylor and Deborah Kerr as its principal stars; both films were released in 1951.

The sequel to '*The Robe*', released in 1953, starring Richard Burton, Jean Simmons, Victor Mature and Michael Rennie, was, '*Demetrius and the Gladiators*', in 1954. Its principal stars were Victor Mature and Susan Hayward. Other cast members included Michael Rennie, Debra Paget, Anne Bancroft and Jay Robinson. The actor Jay Robinson reprised in this sequel, the role he played in '*The Robe*'; he gave another memorable performance playing the cruel Emperor Caligula.

With the obvious attractions offered by the cinema, going out to the cinema was preferable to staying in, as far as Daphne and Dennis were concerned. Like many people, they did not, as yet, own a television.

Besides, going out gave the young couple breathing space; it gave them an opportunity to spend time away from their suffocating living environment. The cinema offered them a welcome escape and a sanctuary away from the unwanted attentions of their interfering landlady.

* * *

Daphne also dreaded the weekends when she wasn't at work on shift duty because it meant that Mrs Trenchard would be constantly looking over her shoulder, watching her as she went about her weekly chores. She would scrutinise the methods Daphne used to do her housework in her usual belligerent manner. She would cast a critical eye over her washing, ironing and general cleaning. Daphne said it was like being back at home, with Mrs Trenchard often interfering in her cleaning rituals, which she said, "left a lot to be desired". Daphne thought Mrs Trenchard was trying to be kind and helpful by giving a new bride tips on how to run a home. But Daphne's husband said Mrs Trenchard was interfering and being bossy.

She told Daphne that housework followed a weekly rota. Monday was always set aside as the wash day. If it rained on Monday then the clothes hung out to dry the following day and finished off inside, draped over every accommodating surface or hung up on make-do lines around the home, to air. Tuesday was generally for ironing. Wednesday was for cleaning out rooms. Thursday was for dusting and polishing. Friday was for baking for the weekend and for the rest of the week. Saturday was for shopping for the weekend.

Shopping was also a daily errand; perishable foodstuffs necessitated daily shopping with the absence of a refrigerator to store these foodstuffs in. (Domestic refrigerators became more affordable for most people in the following decade.) The bigger shop was on Saturday, as virtually everything was, including shops, closed on Holy Sunday. Sunday was a day of rest and reserved for church.

Evenings would be spent darning and mending clothes. The 'make do and mend' philosophy engrained in women from the war and post-war years was a philosophy still adhered to; general shortages and hardships continued in the first half of the Fifties. Although, clothes rationing had ended in March, 1949, utility clothing continued until 1952.

Housewives still followed the same weekly pattern for undertaking their chores. I could never understand why Mondays always had to be a washday? Why did all housewives have to follow like sheep? I heard most women would not even dare hang out their washing to dry on the clothes line midweek for fear of what the neighbours would think! It took a brave mother like mine to not follow suit, but everyone else I knew around that time generally did.

Anyway, Daphne tried to explain to Mrs Trenchard that she couldn't do her chores in the conventional way because she was often busy working during the week. So the evenings and sometimes the weekend was the only time she had to spare to devote to the household chores. Mrs Trenchard pooh-poohed this, exclaiming, according to Daphne's account, that she "should make time!"

Daphne said Mrs Trenchard was becoming too overbearing, constantly dishing out advice to her and treating her like she was her mother. After all, Daphne said she had left home to gain some independence. Mrs Trenchard was always, "proffering", the word Daphne's husband used repeatedly to describe their landlady's, unwanted advice, when it wasn't asked for.

"I wouldn't do it that way, if I were you!" "Look, this is the proper way to do it!" She used to scold Daphne with her retort: "You could learn a lot from watching how I do things!" She always thought she knew best, as she was always saying: "After all, I've had a lot more experience in running a home, so I know what I'm talking about!"

There was no room for mod cons in Mrs Trenchard's kitchen. Daphne said Mrs Trenchard wouldn't hear of using anything that was new or different. She liked to stick with the tried and tested methods of old.

I can recall Daphne telling my mother that she wanted to try new washing detergents that had recently come on the market. Washing powder manufacturers' introduced on the market Tide in 1950, Surf in 1952 and Daz in 1953; Omo was re-launched in 1954.

The competition between manufacturers' of detergents intensified with each claiming their new product made the task of cleaning clothes easier and achieved a cleaner wash. These new products claimed in their advertisements that they were more effective than soap, creating greater 'lather' and a 'whiter' weekly wash. But Mrs Trenchard didn't approve. She poured scorn on these modern washing detergents, saying that: "Nothing beats a bar of green Sunlight soap and some good old elbow grease!"

I also overheard Daphne telling my mother of a humorous incident that happened on a wash day. Mrs Trenchard obviously thought she was doing Daphne a favour by offering her the remains of some hot, soapy water for her to do her washing in after she had finished using it: she didn't want it to go to waste! (Washing clothes was invariably undertaken by hand in the large butler sink (or Belfast sink), housed in the kitchen, usually in the scullery adjacent to the small kitchen; washing machines were still a luxury item for most housewives in the early to mid-Fifties.)

Mrs Trenchard probably developed her conserving mentality from wartime when the population had to learn to live frugally and conserve what they had. She was probably mindful of water being a precious commodity during wartime when it was rationed and so didn't want to see it go to waste. Daphne said Mrs Trenchard expected her to be grateful! She said her husband was more offended than she was when he found out. He was horrified and disgusted at the prospect of his clothes being washed in the same dirty leftover water Mrs Trenchard had also used to wash her underwear in, namely, her large, baggy bloomers!

It was the same with drying and ironing the laundry: Mrs Trenchard would interfere. Sometimes, she would bring Daphne and her husband's clothes in off the line, and once, even did the ironing for her without being asked! On that occasion she had the cheek to complain that Daphne's voluminous skirts and dresses required too much ironing and that it was a waste of material! (This was a common criticism with regard to the full skirts and dresses inspired by the Parisian fashion Designer Christian Dior's 'New Look' of 1947; many viewed it as an unnecessary extravagance during the long period of clothes rationing when material was in short supply.)

Where Daphne thought Mrs Trenchard was trying to be helpful by undertaking her ironing; her husband Dennis had other ideas. He said Mrs Trenchard was not only questioning his wife's ability to iron but more to the point, she was "being nosey", and that it was "too intimate!" He said she more than likely wanted to inspect their clothes, including their underwear: the state of their repair and cleanliness! Dennis said it was worse than being back at home; he found her constant interference suffocating and had had enough, and understandably, couldn't wait to leave.

The young couple felt they had no privacy. Daphne said Dennis always felt uneasy having to endure washing and shaving in the large, deep butler sink housed in the scullery. (I'm not sure whether Mrs Trenchard provided the couple with a wash bowl and pitcher in their bedroom, although, it would have been a laborious process having to fill and empty these after each use.) Daphne said her husband tried to undertake these, "daily ablutions", when Mrs Trenchard wasn't around, which was, "well nigh impossible", according to him.

Of course, many houses being old and also dilapidated back in the first half of the Fifties did not have a bathroom so the occupants had to endure having a strip-wash in the large butler (or Belfast) sink housed in the kitchen or scullery. Bathrooms back then were a luxury and modern convenience. Many families would have to resort to the laborious task of dragging the tin tub from outside in the yard into the kitchen if they wanted a bath, which was often the warmest room in the house. Or they would place the bath tub by an open lit fire in the back room. Family members would then take turns to wash in it, often in the same dirty water, topped up with hot water heated up in a kettle on the kitchen stove. Or if they were more fortunate, from a small domestic water heater, called a geyser. The alternative would be to attend the municipal baths in the town centre, once a week.

Unsurprisingly, Daphne and Dennis couldn't wait to acquire a home of their own. Even if it was one of the new homes under construction, albeit a local authority council owned house. The Housing Act 1949, enabled local authorities to build housing for professionals as well as for manual workers, a point I referred to earlier. What is more, the Housing Act 1952 increased the subsidy given to local authorities for publicly funded building.

At least these new homes would have a bathroom and inside toilet. This was, of course, preferable to using the outside lavatory in all weathers, frequently referred to as the 'privy'. The privy (an outside toilet in a small outbuilding) was often shared by several families in poorer areas, such as in the back-to-back houses (a type of terrace, with only one entry and exit point at the front of the property). The primitive chamber pot would be discreetly placed under beds for night-time use.

The new builds were also adapted to provide central heating. (However, not the modern form of central heating installed in homes in decades to come.) Hot running water was also supplied on tap for bathing and domestic use.

The new council house occupants would no longer have to rely on coal fires, which were extremely labour intensive. (The coal had to be lugged from the outside coal bunker into the house and the coal tipped into the grate from the coal scuttle (a metal bucket with a lip), then the fire had to be lit, stoked, to prevent it from going out, and cleared of ash in preparation for the next fire. The alternative was having to constantly feed the gas meter.) They could now have a constant supply of heat (and light) in every room at the flick of a switch, instead of confined to only one or two rooms that generated heat from a coal fire and/or a paraffin stove. Kitchens were, as I've mentioned before, also fully fitted in these new council homes with integrated appliances. An improved mains electricity supply from the National Grid helped to provide these modern amenities.

Until the time came when Daphne and Dennis would be able to move out they had to grit their teeth and tolerate their present living conditions. While the young couple lived under Mrs Trenchard's roof, she thought she had a right to do as she pleased because it was *her* house. Occasionally, she might knock on their door and make up an excuse that she wanted a few errands done, such as groceries fetched when Daphne went out shopping, knowing of course, that Daphne would never refuse to run her various errands. But her real motive was probably to chat or observe the couples activities, as she could have collared Daphne on the landing or in the hallway with her demands.

More often than not, Mrs Trenchard would enter the couple's rooms uninvited, without knocking first. Daphne found this intrusion particularly upsetting. Mrs Trenchard felt she had a right to enter and inspect their rooms whenever she felt like it, so that she could see if they were treating her furniture and furnishings with respect.

As if this wasn't enough, items started to go missing from the couple's rooms. Since these items belonged to Mrs Trenchard, she thought she was well within her rights to take them without even asking. Daphne complained to my mother about Mrs Trenchard's unreasonable behaviour.

Apparently, Mrs Trenchard's daughter was setting up home with her husband nearby, so she wanted to help her daughter out by providing her daughter with items from her home. Daphne explained to my mother that both she and Dennis had nothing to spare, as they rented sparsely furnished rooms from Mrs Trenchard: she had provided them with only the basics.

In their living room was an old, threadbare three-piece suite, consisting of a two-seater settee and a couple of armchairs. There was also one small, drop-leaf dining table and two dining chairs. The other items consisted of a small occasional table; a standard lamp; a sideboard, and a small paraffin heater. In the bedroom they had an old iron rung bedstead, and a mattress that had seen better days, according to Daphne. Mrs Trenchard also provided them with a couple of blankets and a bedspread. The other bedroom furniture consisted of a bulky, old, mahogany wardrobe and a matching chest of drawers and dressing table. There was also a small table lamp.

They also had another small paraffin heater; that and the heater in their living room provided the only source of heat. Paraffin heaters were the usual form of heating for upstairs rooms. Meanwhile, Mrs Trenchard enjoyed more heat from the open coal fires downstairs in her back and front room.

Covering the cold linoleum floors in Daphne and Dennis' upstairs rooms were a couple of small rugs, which Mrs Trenchard had thrown in for good measure. Whilst a few pieces of cheap bric-a-brac decorated the spartan furniture.

Daphne explained to my mother that Mrs Trenchard always chose her moment carefully before removing items from their rooms. This was when her husband Dennis was out at work, knowing that she would be powerless to object.

It started with small items. First it was a lampshade, "Oh, you won't miss this!" she told Daphne, but Daphne explained to my mother that she didn't like Mrs Trenchard deciding for her. Next, some ornaments went missing, which Daphne said she was glad to see the back of, as these were not to her and her husband's more modern tastes.

Then Mrs Trenchard took from them one of the two small paraffin stoves, which they desperately needed, as the big, old, draughty rooms were often freezing cold. (This was a common complaint from those living in old housing stock back then.) She said they could move the other paraffin heater, which they had in their bedroom to their living room, when they needed it, as they had plenty of blankets on their bed; besides, summer time was soon approaching so they shouldn't require it.

People always seemed to complain about the cold back then and remembered the long, cold winter months of the Forties and Fifties. Imprinted on people's memories was the, 'Big Freeze' of 1947, when Britain experienced the worst winter on record.

The 'Big Freeze' occurred on 24th January, and lasted until 16th March; it brought the country to a standstill. Roads became impassable, cutting the South of the country off from the North. This led to a fuel crisis because coal couldn't be transported, which in turn caused major power cuts effecting industry and homes. The Conservatives initiated the catch phrase, "shiver with Shinwell", because it was Labour's Minister of Fuel and Power, Emanuel (Manny) Shinwell, who badly misjudged fuel stockpiles; as a result, Labour Prime Minister Clement Atlee demoted him.

Most rooms in the home during the Fifties would be often unheated, as the majority of the population couldn't afford to heat all the rooms. Obviously, there was no modern heating system, such as gas central heating; people would have to rely on an open coal fire in the main living room, or heating supplied from a small paraffin heater or a two-bar electric fire.

Anyway, after Dennis protested a little about the loss of one of their paraffin heaters, Mrs Trenchard made out that she would give the young couple a small heater from one of her rooms. Of course, it never materialised so they ended up having to spend their hard-earned cash on one.

The items that were taken from their rooms started to become more frequent and more substantial. Mrs Trenchard removed a floor rug from the cold linoleum floor saying: "I've got a far better one to replace it with." But, of course, the rug she replaced it with, according to Daphne, was "flimsy and even more threadbare!"

Mrs Trenchard even had the audacity to remove from their bed a lovely, soft, silky, quilted, duck feather eiderdown, which Daphne had particularly liked. She exclaimed: "You won't need this eiderdown as I've provided you with blankets. My daughter hasn't got one of these!" She then replaced it with an inferior one, a thinner candlewick bedspread, which didn't have the warm, fluffy down feathers from the eider duck in its interiors! She also had the cheek to take down the curtains from their living room and change these to ones that were even more drab, moth-eaten and threadbare in appearance, making out that the replaced ones were far more suited to the décor of their room.

But Daphne said the final straw was when the bedroom chest of drawers disappeared, which Mrs Trenchard had removed when she wasn't there, with a neighbour's help. She even had the gall to remove all the contents from the drawers and placed them in their room. Her explanation was: "My daughter doesn't have much furniture; besides, you won't have any need for it!" She added that they had more than ample room for their requirements by using the dressing table that she had generously provided them with, and they could always use a small cupboard she had housed on her landing! Daphne thought this was little compensation.

Daphne told my mother that she didn't mind Mrs Trenchard taking things at first because it was items that perhaps she could do without. What's more, she thought she'd be helping Mrs Trenchard out. My mother told Daphne that she was being too obliging. But as the situation got worse it all became too much for Daphne; it upset her, as she felt utterly powerless to object and say anything to Mrs Trenchard, in her defence. She found it difficult to say no, to refuse Mrs Trenchard anything since it was technically Mrs Trenchard's house, in spite of the fact that she and her husband Dennis were paying for furnished rooms.

The couple, on the whole, also didn't like to remonstrate with their landlady because they didn't want to antagonise her and cause any ill feelings while they had to live under her roof. They couldn't afford anything else, besides which, they liked the street they were residing in, and their families probably lived close by, and Daphne's work was within walking distance. Daphne tried to ignore the problem by saying that Mrs Trenchard was not that bad, she had heard of worst landladies. But from what I've heard, Mrs Trenchard took the biscuit!

It was the same with personal items of Daphne's, which would also often go missing, or Daphne would find them in a different place to where she had put them. It was obvious that Mrs Trenchard was entering her room in her absence and using her items.

Daphne found her jar of Pond's Cold Cream, which she had left on her dressing table, elsewhere. Her Lux toilet soap and her hair shampoo, Vosene, (a medicated hair shampoo launched in

Britain in 1949), moved from where she had placed them. Or was it Drene hair shampoo (credited with being the first soapless liquid shampoo). Or perhaps it was the ever popular Silvikrin. Or was it Sunsilk, introduced in Britain in 1954: (although, Daphne may have moved out of her rented accommodation by then).

Her Cussons, Imperial Leather talcum powder, also mysteriously disappeared, and like the other items, often turned up in odd places. Daphne said she couldn't very well accuse Mrs Trenchard of stealing from these items; also it would be difficult to prove so she thought it best to say nothing.

Despite Daphne and Dennis not wishing to make any complaints to their landlady, it seems that she had plenty to complain about when it came to her tenants. Even though Daphne and Dennis were as quiet as mice in their rented rooms, Mrs Trenchard had the audacity to complain that she could hear what few pieces of furniture she had left them with, being moved about above her ceiling. She told them, not only would it wear the linoleum floor covering out but that: "My furniture was not designed to be moved around constantly!"

Daphne said they protested their innocence, saying that what she could hear was them simply walking about and using her furniture and furnishings in a respectful manner, in which they were intended to be used. Mrs Trenchard replied: "In that case, it must be those stiletto heels you insist on wearing; please remove them when you are walking on my floor, as you'll damage the linoleum!" Stiletto shoes were very popular during the Fifties and were often the cause of damaged floors due to the spiky pointed heels.

* * *

The young couple tried to improve their drab and cramped living conditions, after first visiting the, Ideal Home Exhibition (now called the Ideal Home Show), which is an annual event held in Wembley, London. The Exhibition inspired the young couple with innovative ideas. Naturally, Daphne, like all young housewives, yearned for all the newest, labour-saving kitchen appliances.

Daphne was desperate to own her very own Kenwood Chef Food Mixer, with its range of versatile attachments, which could mix, mince, beat, slice and shred, all in one labour-saving product. The product's inventor and namesake, Ken Wood, introduced his revolutionary invention at the Exhibition in June, 1950.

Daphne also wanted what every housewife wanted: the must-have refrigerator and washing machine, the vacuum cleaner and of course, the food mixer. These were the most popular consumer products back in the Fifties. However, most of those, must-have products, such as the washing machine and refrigerator, were luxury items. Daphne and her husband Dennis would have to wait until they could afford them; such items were beyond the affordability of most people back then. Unlike in the United States, where the population were much better off than their counterparts in Britain and so could afford to have these consumer products in their home.

Hire purchase was always an option, whereby Daphne and Dennis would have the wherewithal to purchase these desirable products. But most people, like their landlady, Mrs Trenchard, frowned upon this form of credit, buying 'on tick' or on the 'never-never', as it was called. This attitude, however, was starting to wane with the final lifting of the crippling hire purchase restrictions in 1958.

The population were so hard up after the Second World War that debt was rife, as were the ubiquitous tallymen. These men would travel door to door in poorer neighbourhoods and would keep a tally of the customers they sold their goods and other services to on credit, offered, of course, with high interest rates. This method of credit ensured families would remain in debt for a long time, a never ending debt for many. These families often dreaded the regular weekly visit by the debt collector, so much so that some would hide when he came knocking on their door; they would pretend they weren't in rather than answer the door to him!

I don't think Daphne and Dennis were the type of young couple to get themselves into debt. They weren't struggling with a young family to support who were the sort who often fell victim to the tallyman's weekly visits for his payments. Besides, it was a matter of pride, to be able to save up for items so you were able to purchase them outright, rather than acquiring items on the never-never and ending up in debt.

I expect Daphne and Dennis' first priority was to save up to pay a lump sum to secure a place of their own to live in before attempting to acquire luxury items for the home. In July, 1954, hire purchase restrictions were relaxed, which encouraged consumer spending, but these restrictions were periodically tightened again, thereafter.

The hugely popular Festival of Britain in 1951 showcased revolutionary new products for the home. It also showcased the modernist architecture and urban designs that would feature in the new post-war housing in the newly created towns. The Director of Architecture, Hugh Casson, led the eminent design team, (which included Misha Black, Ralph Tubbs, James Gardner and James Holland) who were responsible for staging the Festival. His name became synonymous with the Festival of Britain thereafter; he was knighted for his services the following year. The Festival of Britain heralded the new changes to come in contemporary living.

Previously, an exhibition entitled, 'Britain Can Make It', staged at the Victoria and Albert Museum in London, exhibited new designs in consumer goods. Its purpose was to showcase the improvements in design in the post war era; this exhibition ran from September to November, 1946. The Furnished Rooms section was particularly popular with the many visitors that went to see the exhibition. This event was organised by the Council for Industrial Design (an organisation set up by the government during the war in 1944 to help restore Britain's economy). It showcased thousands of innovative household products manufactured by over a thousand British firms. Unfortunately, for the British consumer, these products were unavailable under the austerity measures that were in place at the time; the goods were reserved for export. This prompted the British press to rename the exhibition 'Britain Can't Have It.'

The Festival of Britain, Daphne said, inspired them with new ideas for modern living. They went one weekend during the spring or summer of 1951, along with thousands of other festivalgoers. The event held in London, on what was once a bomb damaged site on the South Bank of the Thames, attracted record crowds. An estimated eight and a half million people visited over the period when it was first opened by the then King George the Sixth, on 3rd May, until it closed on 30th September, of that year.

The Festival of Britain marked the centenary of the Great Exhibition of 1851 and was, in effect, a huge trade fair. The Festival provided a post-war boost to the economy; it celebrated and showcased British arts, science, technology and industrial design.

The Festival was a post-war morale booster. It was a 'tonic to the nation', after surviving the deprivations of the recently ended Second World War, according to the Festival's director-general Gerald Barry; (he was responsible for executing the plans for the Festival). The Festival was also a form of celebration. It was 'a pat on the back' for the British people, for what they had endured and sacrificed during the recent war, emerging from it triumphant. This was according to Herbert Morrison, Labour's Deputy Prime Minister, (who initiated the event and advised the Labour Government in his role as Lord President of the Council).

The Festival of Britain staged lots of colourful, themed pavilions. One was entitled, 'The People of Britain', revealing Britain's ancestors through the ages; the 'Lion and the Unicorn' was another, which represented the character of the British people; there was also a 'Sea and Ships' Pavilion, among many others. There were also exhibitions and events, which took place all over the country. The Festival was mainly educational in theme. It was to educate the British public about our country and its great historic achievements, and with a view to looking at modern design and technology of the future.

Daphne said even the café had futuristic furniture with tables and gaily coloured chairs in the Festival colours of red, yellow, blue and grey. She also said the chairs had strange, spindly spiky steel and aluminium legs and many had distinctive tiny ball feet. Earnest Race and Robin Day were the principle furniture designers of the tables and chairs featured at the Festival. Earnest Race designed the famous Antelope chair made from plywood, and aluminium and steel rods, and the stackable Springbok chair made from PVC (plastic) covered springs; Robin Day designed the famous moulded plywood and steel 658 chair, more commonly known as the Royal Festival Hall lounge chair.

There were also futuristic modern sculptures at the Festival. The talking point for everyone that went was the Syklon sculpture, an impressive steel, wire and aluminium vertical structure that stood nearly three hundred feet high above the other structures. (The main structure was approximately two hundred and fifty feet high.) It resembled a tall, slim-shaped cigar that projected into the sky; it could be seen from miles around. Supported only by cables, it appeared to be suspended in mid-air. A newspaper joke at the time, pointed out the similarity between the Skylon and Britain's economy: both had no visible means of support!

Visitors also marvelled at the gigantic, futuristic spaceship-shaped Dome of Discovery, it was the tallest dome in the world back then, standing at ninety-three feet high and three hundred and sixty-five feet in diameter; it dwarfed all the other structures, apart from the Syklon, that is. It contained exhibitions on themes of discovery inside its structure.

Daphne said the whole Festival was, "full of fun, gaiety and colour"; these were some of the buzzwords used to describe the Festival of Britain. Daphne said her favourite part of the Festival was the funfair with its open-air rides and amusements, and the Pleasure Gardens, both sited in nearby Battersea Park. She was particularly struck with the water features, which consisted of a lake and fountains. She said the Pleasure Gardens looked particularly enchanting when illuminated at night; there was also a firework display to light up the night sky. Daphne and Dennis both enjoyed the simple delights of good old-fashioned, open-air dancing that took place in the Pleasure Gardens in the evening.

There were so many attractions to see at the Festival, with something to appeal to everybody, both adults and children alike. Lots of school children visited with their schools, but unfortunately I missed out on going, as I was off school ill and never got another chance to see it. But by all accounts it was worth going to see.

Daphne said she and Dennis both returned from the Festival full of enthusiasm and were keen to make little changes here and there to improve their living arrangements. They just wanted to brighten up the place they were currently living in by introducing new and more colourful furnishings. They wished to add a bit of colour to the drab, dark and dingy furnished rooms with its green and brown old décor, which were the typical colours in conventional home interiors in the Fifties.

Daphne said they got lots of ideas from the 'Homes and Gardens' Pavilion. She found the sample room interior designs inspiring; Daphne described some of the design ideas to my mother and me. The new 'contemporary look' with its plain, clean lines and easy to clean, simplicity style of furniture, they both found particularly appealing. In contrast to the old-fashioned, traditional style, with its over decorated, fussy embellishments and its heavy, bulky, impractical furniture.

Daphne said she wanted a piece of furniture in the new G-Plan design. The British furniture maker, E.Gomme, introduced G-Plan, synonymous with simple, modern designed furniture, not long after the Festival, in 1952. Customers could purchase single pieces without having to purchase a whole suite of furniture. These pieces of furniture could also be utilised in any room. Daphne particularly liked the two-drawer, wooden handled dressing chest on splayed legs, which came in light oak, with a rectangular adjustable mirror. (She needed more drawer space since her landlady Mrs Trenchard had removed a chest of drawers from the couple's room.) This G-Plan dressing chest was one item in the manufacturer's first range of streamlined furniture, named Brandon, introduced in 1953. Like this dressing chest, individual pieces came in light oak, which was very popular, and had wooden handles and the splayed legs that were the height of fashion at the time.

Dennis was particularly impressed with the new futuristic, abstract geometric designs on textiles, wallpaper, ceramics, glassware, lighting and furniture, which were on show at the Festival of Britain. He thought these were an improvement on the traditional floral designs of the old styles.

The advances in science inspired Avant-Garde designers to use scientific molecular and crystallographic structures of boric acid, quartz, aluminium hydroxide, and even haemoglobin (blood) and insulin (a glucose regulating hormone), as the basis for the new abstract designs. These groundbreaking features set the trend in contemporary design.

Daphne was particularly taken with the botanical patterns that were on the furnishings on display at the Festival. Textile designer Lucienne Day, (wife of the Festival's furniture designer Robin Day), exhibited her famous fabric 'Calyx' in the room interiors of the Homes and Gardens Pavilion. A fabric that featured a botanical, abstract geometric printed pattern composed of the cup-shaped outer structures (calyx consisting of green leafy sepals) that enclose a flower bud, with long, thin stalks; this was considered, at the time, a radical design.

Daphne couldn't wait to have one of those new fitted kitchens she saw at the Festival with all the modern, integrated appliances: a cooker, refrigerator and a washing machine. These must-have appliances would fit around built-in storage cupboards and the stainless steel sink, thus utilising the kitchen space.

Formica covered kitchen units, work tops and table tops were the trendsetters in kitchen design in the Fifties, both here in Britain and in the United States. This plastic laminate covering that adorned surfaces, came in an assortment of patterns and an exciting range of colours, such as bright red and yellow. It's hygienic, easy wipe-clean work surfaces were stain and also heat resistant. The unique attributes of this hard-wearing Formica laminate ensured its increasing popularity.

Such kitchen innovations were preferable to having to make do with the old, basic, labour-intensive kitchen with its mishmash of free standing items. These included a kitchen cabinet (if there wasn't a built into the wall larder cupboard or pantry) for storing food, crockery and cutlery; a small stove; a table and chair or two, if there was sufficient room; also a porcelain butler or Belfast sink with a wooden draining board. An adjacent scullery often housed the sink, since the kitchen was usually small and mainly used for cooking; these sinks were large and deep enough to also wash clothes and linen in.

Before the washing machine, doing the laundry was a laborious practice. The scullery was where the laundry was mainly done. A scullery was a small, cold, damp room with a stone floor at the rear of the property, adjacent to the kitchen, which led out to the outside lavatory and coal house (bunker). The scullery usually housed the large butler (or Belfast) sink and a dolly tub, (a large, galvanised wash tub for also doing the washing in); a dolly stick (posser) was a wooden stick-shaped implement with a handle on top used to agitate the clothes in the tub of water. A wooden wash board could also be used to scrub the laundry on. Wooden tongs lifted the clothes from the soapy water for a rinse in the large, deep sink; the bigger items of laundry were wrung through a mangle, if not by hand.

Daphne not only hankered for a modern, multi-purpose, fitted kitchen with all the mod cons, such as the built-in washing machine and refrigerator; she also longed for an open-plan living space, with for example, a kitchen-diner. If this was not possible due to lack of space, then she desired multi-functional rooms created with dual-purpose furniture.

Daphne wanted to create a dining alcove by partitioning off from the main living or sitting room, a separate eating area. The couple could achieve this by using a wall unit of shelves or a large bookcase as a room divider, which they had seen in the showrooms they had visited. Daphne also wanted to introduce a few pieces of light-coloured, slim fitting furniture; she thought of utilising one or two pieces of G-Plan furniture to soften the overall look of the dark mahogany furniture they had in their rooms. But Mrs Trenchard wouldn't hear of it; she flatly refused to entertain these ideas. In order to create more space the young couple politely asked if they might assemble simple constructed overhead shelves in the wall alcoves so they had somewhere to store their books and Dennis's jazz record collection, but Mrs Trenchard was having none of it. It all fell on deaf ears, much to their disappointment.

I even overheard Mrs Trenchard gossiping about the minor changes the young couple wanted to make since their visit to the popular Festival of Britain. She complained to a neighbour: "All of a sudden the furniture I've provided them with is not good enough! It's too bulky!" She continued: "Apparently, my comfortable armchairs take up too much space! I can't see anything wrong with them. They've served me all these years!" She went on: "They asked me if they may replace them with modern ones that have thin, 'spindly', they mean flimsy legs. How absurd! I told them, those won't last long!"

Mrs Trenchard continued to deride their plans for improvement in her usual spiteful tone: "Oh! And they wanted to divide the room off to separate their living room area from the dining area by placing a large open storage unit between the two areas. Of course, I flatly refused to entertain the idea. Getting all these fanciful ideas in their head, whatever next, I asked myself!" She went on: "They barely have two pennies to rub together! On what she earns as a nurse at the local hospital and what he earns in the office where he works in the centre of town. I suppose they intend to buy all these new things on the never-never!" I heard the neighbour's reply, which was a tad sympathetic to their cause: "Oh leave 'em alone Maud, you were young once and newly married!" To which Mrs Trenchard was quick to reply: "Yes, and I recall living with my parents until we could afford to move out; we waited until we got a place of our own before we started making any changes!"

I didn't see Daphne and Dennis much after that. I heard via gossip from Mrs Trenchard that they spent all their spare time, including the evenings, doing wickerwork. They were making things from wicker and raffia, namely, baskets and lampshades.

Basket-weaving was a popular pastime back in the Fifties. Willow twigs, raffia and reed plant fibres and stems are pliable and very versatile materials for use in the craft of basketwork. These can be weaved and plaited into many useful items, from place-mats to various shaped receptacles, such as fruit baskets, sewing baskets and wastepaper baskets. Or if one was more proficient at this craft one could make larger and more intricate items, such as hats, handbags, shopping baskets, picnic baskets and even cradles and chairs. People attended adult education evening classes to learn arts and crafts, such as basket-weaving and leather craft. Night school was becoming popular during the Fifties for those adults that worked during the day.

Mrs Trenchard couldn't understand why her lodgers would want to make lampshades when her lampshades were perfectly serviceable, so she sneered at this hobby of theirs. But I was in on their secret. I knew they had told her a little white lie, which was that it was simply a hobby. They didn't let on, the real reason, which was that this little enterprise was their attempt at making some extra pin money so that they would finally be able to afford a deposit to move into a place of their own.

The post-war Labour Government's plans to clear the many slums and bomb damaged dwellings to make way for the rebuilding of new homes, and even towns had, no doubt, encouraged our young couple in their desire to acquire a place of their own.

The easy and cheap assembly of the prefabricated homes helped Labour to achieve its target figure; however, it did not abate the severe housing shortage. This led to homeless people taking matters into their own hands in 1946, (as I described earlier). These desperate people squatted in disused military camps across Britain, and in abandoned houses and apartments in expensive areas of London, namely in the West End.

The Communist Party staged these private property occupations in a bid to highlight the housing crisis. The incident in the West End involving the communists captured media interest. The Communist Party succeeded in their aim; these cases focused the government's attention on kick-starting the house building programme once more. As a result, many more new homes were built.

Daphne and Dennis were further encouraged by the Conservative Party who won the next general election in October, 1951, on their election pledge to improve the lot of the British people. The population were fed up with living under the harsh economic austerity measures imposed by the Labour Government. The Conservative Party had accurately read the mood of the electorate. Their winning general election slogan in the October, 1951, general election was, '*Set the People Free*'; free from all the restrictions and shortages imposed on them, from food rationing and general shortages of goods, to restrictions on building and on credit. Now, it looked as if all these restrictions were finally coming to an end, which would help Daphne and Dennis to achieve their dream of moving into a property of their own.

The Conservative Party's election promise in 1951 was to also improve on Labour's achievement of rebuilding 200,000 new homes a year. The Conservative's target was to rebuild 300,000 new houses a year. The Housing Minister, Harold Macmillan, managed to achieve this goal year on year; however, most of these were council houses.

The creation of purpose-built new towns in the suburbs under the New Towns Act (1946), offered more places to live, beyond the preserved green belt surrounding major cities. Most of these designated new towns were in the South-East of England in order to ease the population overspill living in overcrowded housing in the Capital. This urban sprawl was to be contained in these newly created towns.

These included between 1946 and 1950, the new towns in Hertfordshire: Hemel Hempstead, Welwyn Garden City, Stevenage and Hatfield; Crawley in West Sussex; Bracknell in Berkshire; Harlow and Basildon in Essex. (Harlow was also the site of

Britain's first high rise, multi-storey block of flats, named, The Lawn, completed in 1951.) Also, a few other new towns were created in the Mid and North-East of England, and in South Wales, and in parts of Scotland.

There was a marked growth in home-ownership in the post-war era. Housing had become more affordable relative to wages. It was an aspiration, particularly among young married couples like Daphne and Dennis to own a home of their own.

If Daphne and Dennis weren't lucky enough to acquire one of the newly constructed homes, their desire would be to obtain one of the old properties still standing after the war and improve it. These were in dire need of modernisation, so the new homeowner was keen to undertake home improvements.

The Housing Act 1949 also enabled local authorities to purchase dilapidated properties for improvement with part of the cost provided for by government funding. More importantly for our young couple was the stipulation that private home owners could be provided with home improvement grants to retard the damage inflicted during the war.

Do it yourself (DIY) was becoming popular once people started to own their own homes, notably in the second half of the Fifties. Becoming proud home owners motivated them to improve their living conditions; they could no longer rely on a landlord or landlady to organise house repairs for them. There was also insufficient money and a labour force to undertake household repairs; these tradesmen were tied up with working on the rebuilding programme after the war. Householders therefore took it upon themselves to do it themselves and hence started the boom in DIY.

A plethora of magazine publications in the second half of the decade helped the DIY market to grow. These provided useful guides, on for example, how to lay a linoleum floor, and how to undertake plumbing and electrical tasks around the home. 'The Practical Householder', was the first British DIY magazine, published in 1955. (The enormously popular, 'Do it Yourself', followed in 1957.)

Practical guidebooks and booklets for the handyman published at the beginning of the century contained instructions and advice on the sorts of tasks more suited for arts and crafts or hobbies. Household repairs were also pertinent to the 'make do and mend' era of the war and post-war years; '*The Home Handyman*', first published in 1950, was in the era of rations and general shortages.

On television an afternoon programme, '*About the Home*', which began in 1951, offered practical home improvement tips to housewives; this led to one of its popular presenter's being given his own show. The '*Barry Bucknell's Do It Yourself*' programme aired in 1957. It made Barry Bucknell a household name and made him the first DIY television personality. DIY became so popular that it led to the staging of DIY exhibitions. The first national DIY exhibition went on show at Olympia, in London, in 1956.

In the first half of the Fifties, easy to use equipment and materials for tackling domestic repairs and minor renovations were on hand for the amateur decorator. The world's first portable electrically powered drill, introduced by Black and Decker, in 1946, entered the British domestic market in the Fifties.

The paint manufacturer Dulux launched their new formulation of alkyd (oil based) paints onto the British market in 1953. Previously professional tradesmen had used this type of paint.

A Chemist working in Britain, named Dr. Salomon Neumann developed Polycell in 1953: the first ready-to-use wallpaper water-soluble paste (made from methyl cellulose). He followed this in 1954 with the methyl cellulose based Polyfilla, an easy, ready-to-use filler to fill in holes and cracks in plaster and wood. (He produced a wallpaper stripper, paint stripper and paintbrush cleaner towards the end of the decade.)

For Daphne and Dennis, their first priority to secure a home of their own would be to save enough capital to put down a deposit and have enough money to repay the mortgage payments. Or they would acquire one of the many local authority owned new council houses for rent that were being built in these new towns. Under the 1952 Housing Act the Conservative Government increased the subsidy paid to councils for house building, as I mentioned earlier.

Daphne and Dennis were, no doubt, counting the days when they would be able to move into a home of their own and would be free from living in the same dilapidated dwelling as their overbearing landlady. Who could blame them for scrimping and saving, and spending every spare second they had with their noses to the grindstone.

Printed in Great Britain
by Amazon